F OREWORD

This report is about the well-being of children and young people, and makes the case that mental health, in its broadest sense, is a subject which needs wider recognition and more attention from all of us. Emotional well-being is central to us all. It is the answer to the question not just, "How are you?" or "How are you getting on?" but, more significantly, "How are you in yourself?" and is fundamental to the way we are each able to live our lives. Though central, it is often a question that is neglected in the way we relate to each other in today's world. This is reflected in the way it easily becomes lost between the boundaries of professionalism, marginal to the focus of the services we provide, and overridden by the structures that we have created in society.

There are signs that many people feel this lack – the phenomenon of the public reaction to the death of Princess Diana was perhaps the most striking. We certainly have been struck by the amount of interest the Inquiry has elicited, both in terms of the volume of evidence that was submitted to us from professionals, parents and children themselves, and the consistency of their views, and in terms of the media interest that the report generated even before it was published.

We hope that it will be read by many different sorts of people, and that it will not only influence public policy and service provision for children and young people in some of the quite specific ways that have been recommended, but will also help to spark a wider debate on the importance of mental health as a subject, and the priority that it should command in all aspects of our national life.

I would like to congratulate the Mental Health Foundation for their courage in undertaking this important and wide-ranging piece of work, and for their persistence in carrying it through, particularly Helen Kay, their Children and Young People Project Manager. Our thanks go to the wide range of people who took the trouble to send us the evidence which has provided the basis of the report. Also many thanks are due to the members of the Inquiry Group who have showed such commitment to the project over the past 18 months and who have contributed so much in terms of their professional expertise and insight. Special thanks are due to those members of the Inquiry who also helped with the writing of the report, particularly David Faulkner and Brenda Allen.

Tessa Baring
Chair of the Inquiry

contents

THE
MENTAL HEALTH
FOUNDATION

Setting the scene

"The problems we are experiencing have been quite devastating, and our child is not yet five. Our worries for the future are immense."

THE SCOPE OF THE INQUIRY

"Unless you have lived with a child who has a mental health or behavioural problem, no matter how hard you try, it is impossible to fully comprehend the effect on the whole family and the range of emotions experienced during one day let alone year after year."

Our work has been motivated by the many stories such as these from parents submitting evidence to our Inquiry. But this report is not only about improving services and care for those children experiencing mental health problems, but also about promoting the general mental health of all the nation's children.

We have taken a broad perspective in an attempt to frame children's mental health within a coherent view of their lives in a changing society. Some reports have looked from a health perspective at services for children with identified mental health problems, and others from non-health perspectives have touched marginally on issues relating to a child's mental health whilst addressing juvenile crime, the criminal justice system, school behaviour, social services and the care system.

In *Bright Futures,* we set ourselves the task of making the connection between these areas by addressing the mental health of all children; the ways in which positive mental health can be promoted, and how it can be restored or strengthened when difficulties arise. In doing so, we do not wish to devalue the claims of those with defined mental illness, but rather to assert their right to be seen as part of a continuum of need – in need of targeted and specialist services, but not stigmatised or excluded. Nor do we wish to undervalue the rights of those children with varying degrees of difficulty to have the help necessary for them to develop into fully participating members of society. It is our firm belief that it is only by promoting the mental health of all children that we can create a mentally healthy society which does not write off vulnerable children.

We will look at what is meant by mental health in children and young people, what factors affect mental health negatively and positively (risk and resilience factors), and how children's mental health can be promoted through interventions and services which range from universal to the highly targeted. We maintain that the responsibility for the development of mentally healthy children rests with us all, as parents, professionals, neighbours and citizens.

Changes in society over the past 20 to 30 years have overturned many of the certainties about the role of individuals and families which formerly went largely unquestioned. Attitudes to children as expressed in the media and even in official documents show contradictory perceptions. These perceptions include seeing children both as innocent victims of physical and sexual abuse, and as heartless and evil killers; as forgotten casualties of a neglectful care system, and as empty intellectual vessels to be filled by the national curriculum; as consumers of expensive games, toys, designer clothing – even fashion accessories themselves.

> "When adults insist that a 'proper' child is an angel with no sexuality, no aggression, no cruelty, then constitutional 'evil' becomes the only way of understanding lies, destructiveness and cruelty." [1]

And if our views of children are ambiguous, our thinking on mental health is even more confused. The media feed us images of 'the mentally ill' as dangerous and unpredictable maniacs who need to be locked up. At the same time Prozac, a drug intended to treat clinical depression, is deemed suitable by some as an aid to tackling the stresses of everyday life. It will not be possible to think clearly about mental health until we accept that we are all 'mental' – that mental health is fundamental to us all and that it is affected by a complex interplay of internal and external factors.

'Mental' is a word which has for too long been seen almost exclusively in negative terms – as a term of abuse within the playground, the workplace or even the family – and when mental is linked with health, the result is often confusion. Yet for all of us the ability to experience emotions, to cope with the ups and downs of life, to make friends and have a sense of identity, is fundamental both to our own well-being, and our ability to contribute individually and collectively to society. Just as physical health is often defined as the absence of physical disease, so too mental health is all too often understood by a narrow quasimedical definition as the absence of diagnosable problems. We want to go beyond such a narrow definition and understanding, and to generate a much wider acceptance of the fundamental importance of promoting the mental health of us all.

MENTAL HEALTH AND ILL HEALTH IN CHILDREN

For a child, mental health means being able to grow and develop emotionally, intellectually and spiritually in ways appropriate for that child's age. The capacity for progress is of utmost importance for children, especially in their relationships with other people. We have developed a new definition of children's mental health, based loosely on that of the Health Advisory Service (see over). In our view, children experience good mental health when they have a number of basic capacities which enable them to make the most of themselves, their relationships and the opportunities presented to them. At the same time, such capacities help them to recover from pain, disappointment and sadness. As stated in Article 24 of the United Nations' Convention on the Rights of the Child, "Health is the basis for a good quality of life and mental health is of overriding importance in this". We believe, in short, that mental health is essential to enjoy life.

It is important that mental health is considered within a cultural context, as each culture has its own ideas about well-being and what promotes this. Different cultures have varying views about the roles and responsibilities of children within the wider family as well as society – what is seen as 'mentally healthy' behaviour may well differ, therefore, from one culture to another. Some stress the importance of children acquiring independence from family, for example, whereas others encourage dependence. Thus, parents place different interpretations on the children's behaviour according to their culture's norms and consequently have different responses to it. A lack of sensitivity to such cultural differences can lead to an increased sense of dislocation for children and a distrust of mental health services on the part of parents.

"Mentally healthy is when you're like disturbed / they feel confused so that if something happens they don't know how to react to it / they cry / lash out and hit people / and get upset over the silliest wee thing." [2]

> **A definition of children's mental health**
> We believe that children who are mentally healthy will have the ability to
> • develop psychologically, emotionally, creatively, intellectually and spiritually
> • initiate, develop and sustain mutually satisfying personal relationships
> • use and enjoy solitude
> • become aware of others and empathise with them
> • play and learn
> • develop a sense of right and wrong
> • resolve (face) problems and setbacks and learn from them.[3]

Mental health problems in children

The mental health of children and young people can be affected by a number of congenital, family, and environmental factors, and they and their families and carers can be faced with
• emotional disorders, eg phobias, anxiety states and depression that may be manifested in physical symptoms
• conduct disorders, eg stealing, defiance, fire-setting, aggression and antisocial behaviour
• hyperkinetic disorders, eg disturbance of activity and attention
• developmental disorders, eg delay in acquiring certain skills such as speech, social ability or bladder control, primarily affecting children with autism and those with pervasive developmental disorders
• eating disorders, eg pre-school eating problems, anorexia nervosa and bulimia nervosa
• habit disorders, eg tics, sleeping problems, soiling
• post-traumatic syndromes
• somatic disorders, eg chronic fatigue syndrome
• psychotic disorders, eg schizophrenia, manic depressive disorder, drug induced psychosis.[4]

Many of these will be experienced only as mild and transitory nuisances to the children and their families, whereas others can have serious and longer lasting effects. A mental health problem can be seen as a 'disturbance in functioning' in one area of relationship, mood, behaviour or development. When a problem is particularly severe or persistent over time, or when a number of these difficulties are experienced at the same time, children are often described as having mental health disorders.

Incidence of mental health problems

There are approximately 14.9 million children and young people under 20 living in the UK, representing 25% of the population. It is calculated that, at any one time, 20% of children and adolescents experience psychological problems. Overall figures from epidemiological studies of children and adolescents spanning years four to 20, suggest that diagnosable anxiety disorders affect around 12% of this age range, disruptive disorders around 10%, attention deficit disorder, perhaps 5%, specific developmental disorders, enuresis and substance abuse up to 6% dependent on age group. Psychotic and pervasive developmental disorders, such as autistic disorder, are very rare, affecting less than 1%.[5]

The majority of children and young people who experience mental health problems have difficulties which can be made much better with early intervention. However, there will always be children who experience more severe disorders, and whose long-term outlook is less favourable. It has been estimated that between 50 and 100% of children with more severe mental health disorders are affected for many years after the initial diagnosis. Those disorders with a particularly poor outcome include pervasive developmental disorders, childhood schizophrenia and attention deficit hyperactivity disorder. Such children and their parents require both specialist services and community-based supports in order to ensure the best possible outcomes.[6]

There is a clear consensus amongst all those working in the field that there have been "substantial increases in psychosocial disorders of youth since the Second World War in nearly all developed countries", and that whilst there is some degree of disagreement concerning the overall prevalence rates for child and adolescent mental health problems within the UK, there is a consensus that rates of recorded problems are rising. The task is to understand what factors are linked with the development of mental health problems and what might protect children from developing problems.[7]

RISK AND RESILIENCE

Evidence has shown that it is possible to identify the factors which have an impact on children's mental health. This provides a framework for recommending effective interventions at the level of the individual child, the child within the family and in the wider social context. Those issues which are known to be associated with the development of mental health problems, the risk factors, will be discussed and then this report will outline some of the factors which are known to protect children (resilience factors). One of the aims of this report is to demonstrate how to reduce the impact of the risk factors and increase children's capacity to develop into mentally competent adults.

Longitudinal studies in the UK, USA and elsewhere in the western world show that a range of factors in children's early lives have been consistently associated with increased risks of problems in adolescence and adulthood. There is considerable overlap between risk factors predicting later mental health difficulties, poor education outcomes, and antisocial behaviour. Thus we know that intervening effectively would yield huge benefits in reducing a number of problems that are of concern to government, school, parents and children.

The risk factors identified for youth crime, for example, often overlap with those for other problems and problem behaviours, such as hard drug misuse, school-age pregnancy, mental health problems and school failure.[8]

With our specific focus on mental health, we see from research into risk and resilience that certain individuals and groups are more at risk of developing mental health problems than others, and that these risk factors are located in a number of areas – risks specific to the child, to their family, their environment and life events. Whilst the processes by which the impact of risk increases or diminishes is not fully understood, currently we know enough about those factors involved to inform policy decisions effectively, especially in relation to preventive and early interventions for children with mental health problems.[9]

Risk

Risk factors are those that increase the probability of a child developing a mental health problem. There is a complex interplay between the range of risk factors in the child's life, their relationship with each other and with the more positive protective factors. Risk factors are cumulative. If a child has only one risk factor in their life, their probability of developing a mental health problem has been defined as being 1-2%. However, with three risk factors it is thought that the likelihood increases to 8%; and with four or more risk factors in their life the likelihood of the child developing a mental health problem is increased by 20%.

We know, therefore, that the greater the number of risks, and the more severe the risks, the greater the likelihood of the child developing a mental health problem.[10]

The following summarises what is known about risk. Risk can relate to the child, family or environment or any combination of these, and provides invaluable indications of when and how to intervene.

Risk factors in the child

Certain individuals have particular vulnerabilities, which have to be understood in relation to their 'assets', their resilience and invulnerability. Boys who have not reached the age of puberty are less resilient than girls in coping with adversity in life. They are also more likely to develop conduct problems,[11] attention deficit hyperactivity disorder and to be autistic than girls. Children with learning disabilities are more at risk of developing mental health problems. One of the reasons may be that it is more difficult for such children to learn positive coping strategies. Children are at increased risk if they have chronic physical illnesses, especially if illnesses are neurological. Children with a 'difficult temperament', and who are less able to adapt themselves to new social situations, are also more at risk of developing mental health problems. Genetic factors may play a part in some mental health problems, but they are unlikely to be the sole cause in most instances, often being triggered by other factors.

Risk factors in the family

Children whose parents have a history of mental health problems, alcohol problems or problems with the law, for example, or who are violent and abusive, are at greater risk of developing mental health problems themselves. Parents' mental health problems, or alcohol difficulties, impact on children indirectly, through the child's relationship with the parent. Volatile and hostile family relationships, and inconsistent and erratic discipline, including violent punishment, pose particular risks. Parental separation and divorce are similarly risk factors for children. Physical and sexual abuse, and a lack of emotional warmth are all important risk factors for children developing mental health problems.

Lack of parental care serves as a vulnerability factor for depression and as a direct risk for conduct disorders and personality disturbance.[12]

Risk factors in the community

Children who are socially isolated, and who are rejected by their peers are at increased risk of mental health problems. It is also known that children who are socioeconomically disadvantaged, eg those living in poverty or who are homeless, are at increased risk, as are children whose families are subject to discrimination.

Risk factors in the child	Risk factors in the family	Risk factors in the community
• Genetic influences	• Overt parental conflict	• Socioeconomic disadvantage
• Low IQ and learning disability	• Family breakdown	• Homelessness
• Specific developmental delay	• Inconsistent or unclear discipline	• Disaster
• Communication difficulty	• Hostile and rejecting relationships	• Discrimination
• Difficult temperament	• Failure to adapt to a child's changing needs	• Other significant life events[13]
• Physical illness especially if chronic and/or neurological	• Physical, sexual and/or emotional abuse	
• Academic failure	• Parental psychiatric illness	
• Low self-esteem	• Parental criminality, alcoholism or personality disorder	
	• Death and loss – including loss of friendship	

The interplay between risk and resilience factors is not yet fully understood. However, children's likelihood of developing mental health problems is greatly increased when adverse external circumstances, adverse family relationships and particular child characteristics reinforce each other. Continuing risk arises from persisting disadvantageous circumstances, rather than from one irreversible early effect.

Whilst biological factors such as early puberty may predispose children to some sorts of mental health problems, changed social circumstances are also important influences. Such changes will tend to have the greatest impact on those who are already psychologically vulnerable, and this applies particularly to such factors as unemployment, divorce, parenthood and stressful life events.

Risk factors operate in a number of ways:
- one adversity may make another negative experience more likely, eg racial discrimination in employment and housing will make it more likely that ethnic groups will suffer the psychosocial effects of personal discrimination, as well as poor housing and employment

- some negative experiences have long-term effects because they shut off important opportunities, eg children attending poor schools are more likely to truant, obtain no or poor qualifications and leave school early[14]

- some risk factors are mediated through their effects on the parents, eg economic pressures on the family may lead to maternal depression which in turn may be associated with marital conflict and impaired parenting which may have a direct effect on boys' psychosocial adjustment.[15]

Risk factors may operate in a somewhat different manner for sub groups of the population under different politicoeconomic conditions, or historical circumstances.

There are stronger associations between poverty and disadvantage and some mental health disorders, including depression, suicide, and serious involvement with illegal drugs. A diagnosis of schizophrenia is also more likely among poorer people, with a relatively high rate of diagnosis among young black men.[16]

Resilience

There are children who, against all the odds, develop into competent, confident and caring adults. Some children are more resilient in the face of stressful life events than others, eg poverty or family discord will impinge more on some children than on others. An important key to promoting children's mental health is, therefore, a greater understanding of these protective factors that enable some children to be resilient – to thrive despite adversity. As with risk factors, those features that serve to reduce the impact of risk or promote the resilience and strength of the children relate to characteristics within the child, family or wider community and can include any combination of these factors.

Resilience factors in the child
Research has shown that children who have an easy temperament as a baby and secure attachment to a parent figure are often more able to cope with adversity in childhood. Girls tend to cope better, as do children of higher intelligence. Those children who have good communication skills, a positive attitude, a problem-solving approach and the capacity to reflect tend to be more resilient. The ability to plan, a belief in control, a sense of humour and religious faith are all qualities that can lead to resilience.

Children who are able to establish a secure attachment to their parents in the first year are better able to manage stressful events later in life.

Resilience factors in the family

Families in which there are four or fewer children, where children are able to maintain contact with their primary carer during their first year of life, and have the opportunity to develop close bonds with at least one carer, can show increased resilience. The presence of substitute parents, such as grandparents or older siblings, neighbours or regular baby-sitters who can act as positive role models, is another factor leading to increased resilience. Resilient boys in particular are those who come from families in which there was a male who could serve as a role model – if not the father, then a grandfather, older cousin or uncle. Maternal employment and the need to take care of younger siblings contribute to a sense of autonomy and responsibility noted in resilient girls, especially where the father is absent.[17]

Resilience factors in the community

Support outside the immediate family, eg close friendships or having access to a network of kin and neighbours, peers and elders for counsel and support, is an important factor in promoting resilience. Also, participating in extra-curricula activities is important. This is linked to the importance of youth or religious leaders enabling young people to acquire a faith that their lives have meaning and over which they have some control.

Resilience factors in the child	Resilience factors in the family	Resilience factors in the community
• Being female • Higher intelligence • Easy temperament when an infant • Secure attachment • Positive attitude, problem-solving approach • Good communication skills • Planner, belief in control • Humour, religious faith • Capacity to reflect	• At least one good parent-child relationship • Affection • Supervision, authoritative discipline • Support for education • Supportive marriage/absence of severe discord	• Wider supportive network • Good housing • High standard of living • High morale school with positive policies for behaviour, attitudes and antibullying • Schools with strong academic and non-academic opportunities • Range of positive sport/leisure activities[18]

Research clearly suggests, however, that as disadvantages and the number of stressful life events accumulate for children or young people, more protective factors were needed to act as counterbalance.

"Resilience seems to involve several related elements. Firstly, a sense of self-esteem and self-confidence; secondly a belief in one's own self-efficacy and ability to deal with change and adaptation; and thirdly, a repertoire of social problem-solving approaches." [19]

An individual is able to cope so long as the balance among risks, stressful life events, and protective factors is manageable. But when risk factors and stressful life events outweigh the protective factors, even the most resilient individual can develop problems. They may be serious coping problems or of the less visible type whose symptoms are internalised.

The evidence suggests that protective processes include those that
• reduce the risk by impacting on the nature of the risk factor itself or altering the exposure to or involvement in the risk
• reduce the likelihood of negative chain reactions arising from the risk
• promote self-esteem and self-efficacy through the availability of secure and supportive personal relationships, or success in achieving tasks

- open up new and positive opportunities and offer turning points, where a risk path may be rerouted.[20]

It is important that consideration be given in developing policies and designing services as to how these protective factors can be universally available. These issues will be discussed throughout this report.

CHANGES IN SOCIETY AFFECTING CHILDREN'S MENTAL HEALTH

There have been a number of changes for better and worse for children in recent decades. On the whole, they are physically healthier, have a longer life expectancy, are better educated and have more spending power than their predecessors. Less positively, they are more likely to experience spells of unemployment, take drugs, suffer psychological disorders, experience parental separation and engage in criminal behaviour.[21]

It is not easy to demonstrate causal links between trends in society and impacts on children and young people. There is an absence of data in a number of important areas, particularly trend data, which makes it difficult to provide a full assessment of the change over time of key dimensions in the lives of children and young people.

There are, however, some changes about which we do have some data and whose impact on the risk of children developing mental health problems is clear. Amongst the most important are changes in employment, the role of communities, income inequality and family structure.

Employment

Changes in the labour market over the past decade have led to increased risk of marginalisation for young people, and particularly young men, who would previously have gained employment without difficulty. The loss of unskilled and semiskilled work places a higher premium on standards of educational achievement not required previously by young people.

'Work rich' and 'work poor' families are examples of a highly differentiated society, in terms of income and the opportunities money buys. Employment can offer other opportunities in terms of wider social contacts, a sense of belonging and contributing. Just over half of the UK's 18 million households have everybody in employment, but the proportion with no one working is increasing and now represents 3.16m or 17.7% of households. Ethnic disparities exist with white households being the more likely to have everybody of working age in employment (54.5%), and ethnic households on average having 20% with no one working.[22]

Although young people are increasingly likely to stay on at school to take A levels, attend a college or undertake a government-supported training, unemployment is higher among young people than any other group. Evidence from the 1991 Census shows that even among the highly qualified, people from minority ethnic groups suffer higher unemployment than white people.

For those in work, there are more demands in terms of the length of the working week with the UK average working week increasing and being substantially higher than fellow EU countries. Juggling other activities and commitments, such as bringing up children or managing one's own or a relative's illness or disabling condition, is now more difficult. Whilst access to employment can be advantageous to parental well-being, with employment reducing the risk of depression in married women with children for example,[23] the increasing demands on those in work is having a negative impact on parents having time to be with their children and exercise supervision and involvement in their lives and activities. Evidence shows this involvement is crucial to children's well-being, and educational development, and diminishes the chances of involvement in delinquency.[24]

Role of communities

Those communities in most need of support networks and extended families have often been adversely affected by structural changes which make those connections increasingly difficult to maintain. Social isolation is a risk factor for mental health problems, and an extended social network a protective factor. Yet many of the mechanisms operating in the social housing market have had negative consequences. They have often resulted in poorer, more disadvantaged households, with lone parents frequently being grouped together in increasingly unbalanced communities. Such communities lack important connections with older extended families and support networks, and are unbalanced in relation to ratios of adults to children and households with members in work and unemployed.

At the most extreme end, this impact can be seen in the numbers of families still living in temporary and bed and breakfast accommodation. Whilst their numbers are falling, such families still account for 15,000 households, with all the concomitant risks to the children through overcrowding, lack of play space, repeated infections and stress-related mental health problems. We cannot expect such communities to find their own solutions to the multiple problems facing them, without structural and appropriate community-based inputs from both government and, at a more local level, agencies able and committed to the process of working in partnership.

Income inequality

There has been a growth in income inequality. The pre-tax differentials are wider than they were in the Edwardian period. In 1990, the top 10% earned 2.5 times the bottom 10% and in 1906 it was 2.4%. The tax burden has been shifted from higher to lower income groups with a concurrent fall in the value of benefits and cuts in public housing. Thirty-two percent of dependent children live in poverty compared to 10% of children in 1979 (using a definition of poverty of below 50% of average income after housing costs).

Poverty, unemployment and bad housing do not necessarily produce inadequate parents, but poverty makes good parenting more difficult. The groups most at risk of poverty are lone parents, families with disabled children, and some ethnic minorities. The adverse impact on children of inequality and poverty includes worse health and educational outcomes and a higher likelihood of being received into public care.[25]

These changes have been compounded by the reduction in the opportunities for free, and in some cases local, public services and activities, such as museums, sports facilities, youth facilities, after-school activities, eg sports, music and drama, opportunities for outdoor adventure, as well as local shopping and transport facilities. Young people without the means to afford such activities are being excluded from an important source of positive experience and self-esteem.

Family structure

Nineteen per cent of children live with one parent and it is estimated that over a quarter of children will experience separation of their parents before they reach 16. Children whose parents separate have a greater risk of achieving less in socioeconomic terms when they become adults, are at increased risk of behavioural problems and tend to report higher levels of depression during adolescence and adulthood in comparison with children of intact families. However, the complexity of factors which impinge on families before, during and after divorce indicates a process rather than a single event – thus conflict, whether it is associated with divorce, or whether it occurs before and after divorce, is a stronger predictor than actual divorce for difficulties for children.[26] Also, research shows that it is family functioning rather than structure that appears to be a better predictor of child outcomes.[27]

PROMOTING CHILDREN'S MENTAL HEALTH

The basis for change

In this context of a rapidly changing society, where people's personal, social and working relationships are shifting, whose responsibility is it to ensure that children grow up mentally healthy? The stresses on the family make it increasingly difficult for vulnerable parents to provide all their children need, yet the roles of government and public services have been changing and their ability to solve social problems has been questioned. There has been an emphasis on public protection and personal safety and on effectiveness and efficiency. To some extent, this emphasis has manifested itself in the development of 'exclusive' solutions that marginalise vulnerable people, eg excluding children from school and increasing the number of those who receive custodial sentences. However, recent government initiatives to promote social inclusion, to support those who are vulnerable, and to strengthen the family are beginning to show other possibilities. Currently, the two approaches coexist and the tensions between them will have to be resolved by hard-pressed practitioners on the ground. Whether they resolve them in an 'exclusive' or 'inclusive' spirit will make a crucial difference to the social effect of the Government's new policies and to many young people's lives.

We support the Government's commitment to promoting 'joined-up' policies and to dealing with complex 'cross-cutting' issues. Their successful implementation should generate examples of good practice in prevention, early intervention and specialist services. Success will, however, demand 'joined-up' implementation at local level, where many of the frustrations of funding mechanisms, organisational boundaries and conflicting targets and performance indicators still remain unresolved. More than that, we will argue that the country as a whole has a responsibility to support and create the sort of society that enables communities to flourish, not least by making children a top priority, locally and nationally.

There is no argument that children need practical skills, such as literacy, numeracy, and technological competence, to cope with the demands of society. But these on their own are not going to equip children with the emotional skills to deal with the increasingly complex worlds of work and relationships. All too often, when reforms are introduced, children and young people's emotional well-being and competency, their mental health, are neglected. These should be given as much priority as any of the other aspects of children's lives.

We concur that it is important to *"create an emotionally literate culture, where the facility to handle the complexities of emotional life is as widespread as the capacity to read, write and do arithmetic".*[28]

As a nation we have to change our attitudes towards children, to embrace the possibilities of developing an inclusive society in which children and young people's contributions and roles are valued and their well-being promoted by everyone. Society should not allow those who seem to be different, to be 'other', to be further excluded from it.

Mental health care in general suffers from a lack of funding, and services for children and young people experiencing mental health problems are particularly starved of resources. Recent reports,[29] most notably the Health Select Committee report on services for children with mental health problems, see lack of services, lack of funding and lack of priority given to this area as being areas of real concern.

The Health Services Committee report was concerned with the issue of children's and young people's mental health principally from a narrow health perspective. We want to go much further than this. The majority of children with mental health problems never reach specialist services,[30] and have to rely on families, local communities, schools and primary care agencies.

Throughout this report, we will argue that it is vital that the country as a whole recognises that members of families and extended families, informal networks of friends and acquaintances, community and faith groups, and local charitable organisations all have a responsibility towards all of our children. Government in turn has a responsibility to create the structures and climate to facilitate us in this task.

Mental health problems do not develop from isolated causes. They are often the results of, and responses to, complex and as yet not fully understood combinations of influences, including risk and resilience factors within the child, their family and the broader social and economic contexts. Therefore, any response to meeting the needs of children and young people has to operate at a number of levels. These levels, in many instances, concern ordinary citizens and those children with whom they have contact in the course of their personal and professional lives.

Financial considerations

There are numerous reasons for which increased spending in the area of children's mental health should be regarded as a good investment.

In 1971, children under 20 comprised 31% of the population, by 1996 this figure had fallen to 25%. In comparison, the numbers of over retirement age 60/65 have increased from 17.9% in 1984 to 18.2% in 1995 – thus children as future workers and carers will be an increasingly precious resource. It is therefore to all our benefit to ensure that all children are nurtured to enable them to reach their full potential.

This responsibility is particularly important for those children who are more at risk of developing mental health problems than other children. Changes in society may be inevitable – some predicted or planned, some unexpected or outside the control of government. The greatest impact may be felt among the poorer, more vulnerable groups and individuals in society.

Developing the environment for mentally healthier children and young people creates a healthier environment for other age groups too. Firstly, all age groups tend to live in relatively close proximity to each other – thus a higher quality environment for children will have positive benefits for everyone. Secondly, mentally healthier young people are less likely to underachieve or be drawn into antisocial activities with the misery and costs that this engenders for other people. They are also more likely to be actively and positively contributing to their neighbourhood and social economy and, in time, fulfilling their own role as parents and citizens.

The impact for children of having mental health problems is often multifaceted in nature, affecting the whole range of the child's social and educational opportunities. For example, emotional and behavioural disorders can often interfere with education. If this results in poor attainment, with attendant low self-esteem, there is the risk of developing further psychological problems, compounded by social isolation and poor peer relationships.[31] Low educational attainment produces reduced opportunities for the individual for employment and a reduced likelihood of a well educated labour force. In addition to this, some mental health problems/disorders in childhood, if not adequately treated, persist into adult life with an enduring legacy, negatively impacting on the individuals' social life and potential economic contribution.[32]

Mental health problems in children increase demands on personal social services, education, health and juvenile justice services. It is also costly for families. In a study of conduct disorder that also examined the distribution of costs, the following figures for the yearly costs emerged.[33]

Distribution of the costs of conduct disorder in children
- 19% National Health Service
- 7.6% Social Services
- 36% Local Education Authority
- 0.4% Voluntary sector
- 37% Families

These figures, showing the greatest costs of such children falling on families, schools and their education authority, beg the question – is this why it has been so easy to ignore them? Part of the answer could be that the costs after childhood for such children do not fall on the health service, but on youth justice and benefit agencies. As they grow older, children who had conduct disorder have a greater likelihood than their peers of becoming involved in the criminal justice system, and all the expenditure that this incurs. For example, the National Health Service provides services for people suffering from the physical and psychiatric conditions of drug abuse and alcoholism. These conditions are frequently chronic. Law enforcement agencies, intermediate treatment facilities and the probation service have to detect and prevent delinquency and bring to justice those people who exhibit delinquent behaviour. The cost of these activities must be added to that of personal and property damage. The rate of unemployment and social security benefits going to young people who had conduct disorder is far higher than to those who did not.[34]

Preliminary findings from a study of the lifetime costs of conduct disorder up to age 28 found that those individuals who had had conduct disorder aged 10 cost over £100,000 more in services used than those without conduct disorder.[35]

In a presentation to the Inquiry, Scott was able to make a strong case for the cost-effectiveness of early interventions. He argued that if conduct disorders affecting 5% of the childhood population and costing approximately £100,000 until the young person was 26 could be reduced to those of problems, affecting 10% of the childhood population and costing 'only' £70,000 per child, savings of £30,000 could be made for each child initially experiencing conduct disorders. Thus the cost benefit of early intervention is large, even if the treatment effect is moderate. When added to the emotional and social benefits for the child, their family and society at large, this work has clear implications for the choices that society can make in relation to vulnerable children.[36]

Society's choices

The UK is a signatory to the United Nations' Convention on Children's Rights which clearly states that all children and young people under 18 have the right to "enjoy the highest attainable standards of (mental) health and to facilities for the treatment of illness and rehabilitation of health". States Parties shall "strive to ensure that no child is deprived of his or her right of access to such health care services".[37]

The country has therefore signed up to the right of all children to the highest attainable standard of mental health. It must ensure that this is more than just a paper commitment. The Inquiry has considered some of the societal changes that have led to the marginalisation of many of the more vulnerable or disturbed members of society. The effects of such marginalisation of children are seen, for example, in the increasing numbers of school exclusions and the hardening of attitudes in the criminal justice arena.

The demonisation of those young people with mental health problems or disruptive behaviour has enabled troubled and troublesome children to be portrayed as being the preserve of the mental health professionals or the criminal justice system, not the concern of society as whole. This is in part a reaction to the insecurity and instability that has affected society as a whole and made it less tolerant. However, there are signs that people are increasingly seeing that everyone may benefit from a more just and stable society with a strong sense of citizenship. The development of notions of rights and responsibilities could lead to the revival of public values and the increasing sense of civil society. It is this civil society – encompassing the voluntary sector, and also less formal associations and relationships – which provides opportunities for personal development, service to others, and support in times of difficulty – the building blocks of communities. It includes cultural minorities not as separate groups, to be assimilated or tolerated on the 'majority's' terms, but as equal members of a single nation or society entitled to equal consideration as citizens and sharing a mutual sense of equal respect.

Communities are not equal in their abilities to promote informal supports and associations. This does not mean that such networks are not vitally important, and an effective role of local government and other voluntary agencies should be to promote and support their development. We believe that it is vital that such 'inclusive' community responses are particularly appropriate for and targeted at those who are the most vulnerable, and least likely to access universal services. Thus, while it is everyone's responsibility to promote children's mental health, no one operates in a vacuum; and there are complex relationships between individuals and groups involved in supporting children, promoting their well-being. Structures and services in existence facilitate this.

Promoting children's well-being benefits everyone. It can raise the general standard of values and behaviour from which everyone benefits. Its failure can result in a deterioration in behaviour and attitudes in a community to a point where in some areas there is a social collapse which is difficult to reverse.

There is also a real need to improve public and professional understanding of the links between health, education and economic policy and the consequences for everyone of the increasing social and economic exclusion of a substantial proportion of the population.[38]

In the light of all that we know about how to improve children's chances of growing up, society is now at risk of allowing a marginalised and vulnerable group of children to become further alienated and grow from troubled and troublesome youths into excluded and feared adults. Or it can implement the changes in policy and social organisation which gives these children a chance. The choices are not just whether the country is prepared to fund a range of services at all levels rather than just a safety net, but whether citizens as individuals and professionals are also prepared to make a commitment to an inclusive and reciprocal social structure.

Attitudes to children and young people need to change. Children are still developing and need help to enable them to reach their maximum potential. A focus solely on the problems they create for others will not enable them to be brought more effectively into benefiting from, and contributing to, society. In times of economic uncertainty, surely it is all the more important to set priorities to ensure that children have the emotional and social supports needed to meet tough challenges ahead.

FINDINGS OF THE INQUIRY

This report analyses the issues, presents conclusions drawn from the evidence and makes recommendations for change. Chapter Two develops ideas of how to promote the mental health of all children through universal interventions which can support families in the parenting task and which can enable children to develop the emotional literacy and self-esteem which increase their resilience. In Chapter Three, we examine the importance of early intervention for those at high risk of developing problems or those beginning to manifest difficulties and show how mainstream services can provide access to help. Chapter Four looks at specialist mental health services for children and young people. The needs of young people who can no longer be seen as children is considered separately in Chapter Five. In Chapter Six, we describe the way forward and set out the action we believe necessary for individual agencies.

1 Observer 28 March 1993

2 Armstrong, C Hill, M and Secker, J (1998)
Listening to Children Mental Health Foundation, London

3 Source: based loosely on Hill in NHS Health Advisory
Service (1995) *Together We Stand. The Commissioning Role
and Management of Child and Adolescent Mental Health
Services* HMSO, London

4 Kurtz, Z in NHS/HAS (1995) as in no 3

5 Target, M and Fonagy, P (1996) *The Psychological
Treatment of Children and Adolescent Psychiatric Disorders*
in Roth, A and Fonagy, P *What Works for Whom:
Implications and limitations of the research literature*
(pp263-320) Guildford Press, New York

6 Target, M and Fonagy, P (1996) as in no 5

7 Rutter, M and Smith, D J (1995) *Psychosocial Disorders
in Young People. Time trends and their causes* John Wiley
& Sons Ltd

8 Rutter, M Giller, H Hagell, A (1998) *Antisocial behaviour
by Young People. A Major New Review of the Research*
Cambridge University Press

9 John Graham quoted by David Utting in *Suggestions for
the UK, an overview of possible action* Seminar paper,
Cross Departmental Spending review of provision for young
children HM Treasury 1998 vol 1

10 Evidence to the Inquiry from Professor Peter Hill,
The Hospital for Sick Children, Great Ormond Street

11 Rutter, M (1979) *Protective factors in children's
responses to stress and disadvantage* in Kent, M W and
Rolf, J E (Eds) *Primary Prevention in Psychopathology vol
3 Social Competence in Children* Hanover N H University
Press in New England, pp49-74

12 Farrington, D P and West, D J (1981) *The Cambridge
Study in Delinquent Development* (UK) in *Perspective
Longitudinal Research. An empirical basis for the primary
prevention of psychological disorders* (eds Mednick, SA and
Baert, AE) Oxford University Press, pp133-145

13 Pearce, J and Holmes, S P (1994) *Health Gain
Investment Programme. Technical Review Document.
People with Mental Health Problems (part four) – Child
and Adolescent Mental Health* NHS Executive Trent and
CMHSD

14 Quinton, D and Rutter, M (1988) *Parenting Breakdown:
The making and breaking of intergenerational links*
Avebury, Aldershot

15 Rutter, M and Smith, D J (1995) as in no 7

16 Dennehy, A Smith, L and Harker, P (1997)
Not to be Ignored, Young People, Poverty and Health
London CPAG/ Kings Fund

17 Luthar, S S and Zigler, E (1991) *Vulnerability and
Competence. A Review of Research on Resilience* in
Childhood American Journal of Orthopsychiatry
vol 61, pp6-22

18 Adapted from Scott, S Rutter, M and Hindley, P evidence
to Health Select Committee 4th report, Child and
Adolescent Mental Health Services report and proceedings
The Stationery Office, London 1997

19 Rutter, M (1985) *Resilience in the face of adversity.
Protective Factors and resistance to psychiatric disorder*
British Journal of Psychiatry vol 147, pp598-611

20 Rutter, M (1990) *Psychosocial Resilience and Protective
Mechanisms* in Rolfe, J Masten, A S Cichetti, D
Neuchterlein, K H and Wentraub, S (eds) *Risk and
Protective Factors in the Development of Psychopathology*
Cambridge CUP

21 Rutter, M and Smith, D J (1995) as in no 7

22 Labour Market Trends (August 1998) HMSO, London

23 Brown, G and Harris, T (1979) *Social Origins of
Depression* London Tavistock Publications

24 Luthar, S S and Zigler, E (1991) as in no 7

25 Acheson, D (1998) *Independent Inquiry into Inequalities
in Health Report* The Stationery Office, London

26 Amato, P and Keith, B (1991) *Parental divorce and the
well being of children; a meta-analysis* Psychological
Bulletin vol 110, pp24-46

27 McFarlane, A Bellissimo, A and Norman, G (1995)
*Family Structure, Family Functioning and Adolescent Well-
Being: the Transcendent Influence of Parental Style* Journal
of Child Psychology and Psychiatry vol 36, pp847-864

28 Orbach, S (1997) quoted in *Realising the Potential: Emotional Education for All An Antidote report*

29 House of Commons Health Committee (1997) Fourth Report, *Child and Adolescent Mental Health Services: Report and proceedings* The Stationery Office, London NHS Health Advisory Service (1995) *Together We Stand. The Commissioning Role and Management of Child and Adolescent Mental Health Services* HMSO London (1997)

30 Target, M & Fonagy, P (1996) as in no 5

31 Kurtz, Z (1996) *Treating Children Well* Mental Health Foundation, London

32 Target, M and Fonagy, P (1996) quoted in Kurtz, Z (1996) as in no 31

33 Knapp, M Scott, S and Davies, J (1999) *The cost of antisocial behaviour in young children: preliminary findings from a pilot sample. A pilot of economic and family impact* Journal of Clinical Child Psychology and Psychiatry in press

34 Rutter, M and Giller, H (1983) *Juvenile Delinquency: Trends and perspectives* Penguin

35 Knapp, M and Scott, S (August 1998) *The impact of psychotherapy on the lifetime cost of childhood conduct disorder* unpublished report for the Mental Health Foundation

36 Evidence to the Inquiry from Dr Stephen Scott, Institute of Psychiatry

37 Article 24 of the 1989 United Nations' Convention of the Rights of the Child, ratified by the United Kingdom in 1991

38 Watt, G C M (1996) *All together now: why social deprivation matters to everyone* BMJ vol 312, pp1026-9

Promoting children's mental health

CREATING A HEALTHY CLIMATE

"It is those services that are made available to every family in the land, which have had a major impact on the nation's health and welfare. Such diverse elements as compulsory education, mass immunisation and mains sewerage and the creation of a National Insurance system can be numbered amongst the landmarks for improving health and welfare." [1]

It is this aspect of policy, a public health approach to promoting children's mental health through universal services, which we believe is the way forward.

We know enough to be clear that promoting all children's mental health should result in especially high returns for vulnerable groups, eg children in care, children living with a mentally ill parent, and that such promotion work is particularly effective when delivered within existing communities. Children and young people themselves told us that family, friends, informal networks and mainstream services were the most important sources of emotional well-being.

In a society in which many of us no longer have immediate access to a supportive family or close-knit community in which to ask for help or advice, it is vital that more professionally-based advice and support is seen as being 'normal' – that we create a climate in which it is both acceptable and possible to ask for help. Thus, in order for support for parenting to be universally accepted as normal, it has to be universally available through schools, clubs and other non-stigmatising settings. It is important to bear in mind that universal availability will not be achieved without an understanding of what enables services to be accessible to people. Cultural sensitivity, location, timing, attitudes of staff will all affect whether people believe services are welcoming. Special effort will have to be made to reach those who feel excluded or are fearful of criticism and blame.

This chapter will reflect what we learned about what is helpful in promoting positive mental health. The initiatives described are those that, through universal availability, could have an impact on everyone. Many of these initiatives will be aimed at families, given their primary role in children's lives, but there is also a place for schools and community-based mainstream agencies to provide positive input to children's mental health development.

PROMOTING CHILDREN'S MENTAL HEALTH THROUGH THE FAMILY

Research into risk and resilience has clearly shown the fundamental role that families have in promoting children's mental health. The changing structures of families, the factors contributing to this, and their potential impact on children have all been the subject of numerous research projects and reports.

Not only has the family changed, but the social environment has changed in ways that make it harder for parents to provide the good care which will be the basis of their children's healthy physical and emotional development. There needs to be a recognition that parenting is not an intrinsically private act, but that family life is constructed around a network of relationships within a larger setting of community, social and legal structures. Policies should be based not on blaming the child and parents when things go wrong, but on supporting parents in the parenting task. This justifies a range of initiatives from more public provision for parent education through to national policies on employment, taxation, housing, health and social services which help parents.

Support for parents

"Good parenting requires certain permitting circumstances. There must be the necessary life opportunities and facilities. Where these are lacking, even the best parents may find it difficult to exercise their skills." [2]

Parenting education and support can have a vital role to play for all parents, contributing towards the creation and promotion of a "cycle of development and hope".[3] Many of the initiatives to increase parents' support and confidence in their role are currently banded together under the heading of parenting education and support. Parenting education "describes a diverse range of educational and supportive activities that help parents and prospective parents to better understand and address their own personal, emotional, social, intellectual and physical needs, as well as those of their children. These activities usually contribute to a supportive network of services within local communities and help families to take advantage of them".[4]

Support for parenting includes all those involved in the care of children and "focuses more specifically on the emotional and psychological processes and style of parenting. It recognises that parenting does not 'come naturally'; it is not instinctive but learnt – usually, for good or ill, from our own parents – and that love does not, alone, secure the child's parenting needs".[5]

There are a number of key transitions in the life of all families when parents may benefit particularly from support especially as they are likely to be seeking practical information and advice at those times. These are most notably in
- the period around the birth of the first child (and to a lesser extent during the child's first five years)
- the transition to school at four/five years
- the transition to secondary school at 11
- the transition from school.

Practitioners and researchers have found that these are times when parents are usually more open to support and educative approaches.[6] At these times, parenting support can be presented in a non-stigmatising way, as being available and appropriate for everyone, and can provide an accessible gateway for more specialist services for those who require it.

In this section, we will examine ways in which parenting education and support aimed at promoting children's mental health can be delivered. The majority of the evidence, relating to both research and initiatives on the ground, is focused on mothers, the roles and responsibility of fathers being given much less emphasis.

"Don't shut out the parents. We do the caring whatever the age of the young person. It's hard to do it in isolation. We need more information and support."

Parenting education for young people

An important aspect of parenting education and support is that it is universal and should begin early. The Government has recognised the importance of parenting education within schools. The Inquiry heard evidence from the Children's Society on the work that they have been carrying out in relation to parenting education in a number of schools.

PARENTING EDUCATION IN SCHOOLS – PROJECT RUN BY THE CHILDREN'S SOCIETY

In 1994, the Children's Society launched a pack *Education for Parenthood*, to provide a grounding for school students and other young people in understanding what it means to be a parent. The pack is designed to fit into Key Stage 4 of the school curriculum (14-18), although it can also be adapted for use by family centres, and youth groups, etc. The aim of the pack is to provide material which can be used either for short sessions to 'slot into' specific school programmes, such as a Personal and Social Education course, or which can be developed for more substantial theme or project-based work. An important focus of the work of the project, is on the emotional aspects of parenting:

- emotional bonds
- getting along together
- handling difficult situations.

By seeking to explore these ideas in the (relatively) safe context of the school, and by resisting the temptation to target families designated as having problems or children defined as being difficult, the pack is designed to offer a way of exploring potential family conflicts and tensions in a way that is unthreatening but still enables practical and useful lessons to be learnt.

The schools taking part in the study include a Catholic school, an all boys schools, and a school where 75% of the pupils are of minority ethnic origin, predominantly Asian. Each school adapted and delivered the programme in different ways; some taught the material in a straight forward manner through the PSHE programme, whilst others are developing cross curricular activities, and some have developed project work. Whilst the full evaluation of the project has not yet been completed, certain initial achievements of the project are of interest:

- very broad enthusiasm for the project has been identified across all the schools
- potentially difficult and problematic areas, such as poor relationships, violence and mistreatment have been discussed thoughtfully and sensitively.

The lessons from this work are the importance of
- adopting an approach which does not seek to target those who are seen to be potential 'failures' as parents
- not promoting specific messages which imply the superiority of one particular religion or culture.

"It is intended to acknowledge and hopefully celebrate diversity in family life. This is important if we are to encourage an open attitude towards learning about parenthood, where stereotypes and prejudgements abound. If there is a moral message to this work, it is that parenthood is an important and responsible undertaking, it needs to be approached in an informed and caring manner, and it needs to be done well." [7]

Pre and post-birth supports to parents

It is generally acknowledged that all parents require support and help around the time of the birth of a child and universal services are considered an absolute necessity. Our evidence has suggested that such universal support should begin early and that preparation for parenthood should be a key component of all pre-birth support work.

There is growing evidence that maternal stress in pregnancy has an adverse effect on infant birth-weight as great as the effect of smoking[8] and that this stress may also be associated with both depression and behavioural problems in the baby later on.[9] Maternal stress in pregnancy appears to have an adverse effect on the development of the brain in utero, although the psychological mechanisms are not yet fully understood.[10] Stress is not confined to a high risk group, but "many women and their partners experience low to moderate levels of anxiety and depression in their transition to parenthood".[11]

It is clear, therefore, that much more should be done to prepare all parents for the emotional changes in their lives after the birth of their baby, including how to respond to their babies' emotional needs. Research has shown that mothers who are supported in pregnancy are psychologically more healthy, suffer less anxiety and depression and experience more satisfaction in their relationships both with their baby and their partner. In addition, their babies are calmer.[12]

In Britain every year, almost 300,000 women give birth to their first child, while over 400,000 give birth to a second or subsequent child.[13] It is clear from the evidence that presently there is very little 'preparation for parenthood' actually taking place for mothers and fathers to be.

"Currently, British antenatal classes are found to be generally poorly designed and run, to start too late in pregnancy, focus mainly on women, childbirth and practical aspects of infant care, with inadequate teaching on parenting issues and human sexuality, and exclude men." [14]

In addition, the percentage of women currently attending antenatal classes is low, with fewer 'at risk' parents attending. Estimates suggest that on average, only 10-15% of women, and 6% of their partners attend any sort of antenatal class. Only 2% will attend private classes, of the sort provided by the National Childbirth Trust.[15] It is clear that supporting families at this critical time could have major benefits for all families, as well as identifying those at risk.

Recommendation: The Department of Health should look at developing ways in which universal pre-birth support for all parents could begin early and be based on the assumption that preparation for parenthood is 'normal', not merely for 'at risk' families. Such support should provide an opportunity to explore emotional and relationship issues, alongside offering practical advice and support.

The provision of such universal supports could provide important opportunities to screen and ensure additional help was available for those at greatest risk (for a further discussion of these issues see Chapter Three).

"I couldn't face telling anyone because I thought that it was all my fault – and so we all pretended that it wasn't really happening./ If only I knew then what I know now, we might have saved ourselves years of unhappiness."

The Government has recognised the importance of post-natal supports in the Green Paper – *Supporting Families*, with its commitment to expanding the role of health visitors from a narrow health focus to supporting families more generally. We believe this role should start with antenatal support for all women, but with particular targeted approaches to those most at risk. Currently the distribution of health visitors is patchy and their role differs greatly from area to area. GP training will need to include the importance of the role of health visitors in the area of relationships and emotional development. Primary Care Groups should support the development of this extended health visitor role within each locality.

Recommendation: As it develops its policy on the family, the Government should address the distribution and role of health visitors. Spending plans should make adequate provision for the recruitment and training of new health visitors. In particular, areas of high morbidity or where parents are isolated because of location or ethnicity, will require higher levels of provision. In order to ensure equity of provision between communities, we would expect the Government to give clear guidance on numbers, resources and training.

We warmly welcome the Government's *Sure Start* initiative which will target universal services at those communities who are disadvantaged. The implications of this important initiative are discussed in more detail in Chapter Three. However, we would want to ensure that within all those services provided under the *Sure Start* initiative, attention is given to the provision of support to parents and children in relation to mental health.

Supports available to parents and children at times of transition or change

There are a number of key transitions in children's lives which can be experienced more or less positively. Starting nursery or school, choosing schools, moving house, experiencing change in family structure such as new siblings, separation of parents, bereavement, new parental partners are all significant events in a child's life. At times of transition children will experience a range of emotions which may include excitement, grief, anger, distress, sorrow. Some children will apparently sail through very difficult circumstances and others will be upset by minor events. Adults need to be sensitive to children's feelings and accepting of them and to give children the opportunity to talk and feel supported in their everyday world, extended family, schools, general practitioners.

Loss and absence of all kinds, including, for example, bereavement or parental illness, can have negative effects on children, but an area of particular concern for the Inquiry was the range of support and advice currently available to both parents and children during and after parental separation or divorce.

Recent research has highlighted key factors relating to the potential impact of parental discord, divorce or separation on children. As we have already discussed in Chapter One, research[16] suggests that the potentially negative impact of separation on children, resulting in children being at increased risk of behaviour problems, and being more at risk of depressive symptoms during adolescence, is not a result of simple cause and effect. The effect of separation has to be understood as a process in which conflict before and after divorce, the impact of the separation on parents, are as likely to impact on the children as the divorce or separation itself. It is important that children have someone to talk to about their experiences during this period. Research shows that parents often fail to appreciate the extent of their children's unhappiness during this period, and that the adults to whom children would normally turn to when distressed (their parents) are themselves preoccupied and distressed.[17]

Comprehensive support for families at that point in the transition from one family structure to another is likely to ameliorate immediate distress and may have long-term benefits. The Family Law Act 1996 has the potential to reduce acrimony through mediation, but support needs to be provided from a variety of sources and a range of geographical locations. These could include general practitioners, teachers, family lawyers and counsellors.

Recommendation: The National Family and Parenting Institute should be tasked with ensuring that information and support are readily available from mainstream services for parents and children during any periods of family break-up. Services set up for adults, such as Relate, should also develop support services specifically for children.

Parenting programmes

There have been important recent developments in parenting education and support through parenting programmes. Parenting programmes can be for parents who want to do a 'good enough' job of parenting, those whose children have behaviour problems, in either the normal or the severe range, and parents with multiple problems and very low self-esteem.

Programmes for those parents who want to do a 'good enough' job tend to have a completely open access approach. For example, those delivered by agencies such as Pippin, the Family Caring Trust and Parent Network fall under this category. Initiatives aimed at parents whose children have behavioural problems, or at parents with multiple problems and low self-esteem, will be discussed in Chapter Three.

Genuine accessibility is a key for programmes aimed at all parents. In many areas, such programmes are not available, are only available to parents whose children are attending particular schools, or are overly expensive for all parents. Many of the parents submitting evidence to us highlighted their initial reluctance to gain help or support for fear of being labelled as having failed.

We want to ensure that support and help is available for all parents, and that to ask for help is seen as being a normal thing to do. There is also evidence that few fathers attend the majority of parenting programmes, except for programmes specifically designed for couples, eg Pippin.

Recommendation: All parenting support programmes should develop opportunities to engage fathers, particularly the most vulnerable, and to encourage them to build positive relationships with their children and increase their confidence and self-esteem.

"The thing is – you're not taught the best way to be parents. You have to do the best you can as you go along." [18]

POSITIVE PARENTING

Based in Durham, *Positive Parenting* is a programme for parents run as either single workshops or a series, based on schools, community centres, family centres, etc. The objectives of the course are to empower parents to recognise their existing skills and to prioritise and work systematically towards clear, planned targets. A strong problem-solving approach underpins all the materials.

The courses are funded by GEST, City Action/City Challenge, and the Employment Service (Department of Employment). An evaluation of the effectiveness of the training for parents (Penny 94) found that parents recognised that they were already experienced in the highly complex skills of parenting; parents learnt new approaches to child management; they felt valued partners in their children's development and that they felt valued as adults who were worthy of investment and training.

In a recent survey of parenting and parents' needs, carried out by Exploring Parenthood through Sainsbury's magazine[19] over 60% of the 14,000 parent respondents said that they would welcome parenting skills training if it were available. This indicates the potential interest in such services, if they were widely available and effectively promoted as being a positive resource for all parents. In order to achieve this, and ensure that courses are open to everyone, especially those who are more difficult to reach, practical aspects of accessibility, such as location, cost and time of day need to be carefully considered and agreed with members of local communities.[20]

Recommendation: There should be open access or self-referral to parent support services. Such services should be able to draw support and advice from more specialist services, in order to meet the differing levels of need, and, where appropriate, refer on to specialist services.

Informal and community-based supports to parents

As we will argue throughout this report, the role of promotion and prevention in relation to children's mental health is to strengthen the ability of individuals, families and communities to cope with problems as they arise. As traditional structures break down with increased mobility and changes in family patterns, other social structures are needed to provide stability and security. Informal networks and those run by voluntary organisations were highly valued by those who gave evidence.

"The parents group was great, it gave us an opportunity to meet other parents who were having similar problems to us. I wasn't ashamed of going, and it wasn't patronising or anything. We felt that we weren't the only ones you know - and it helped us to think through how to cope better." [21]

Such networks, operating at a community level, provide a sense of belonging, opportunities both to receive help and support, and to offer it to others – processes that are the building blocks of communities.

"My faith has enabled me to cope, and at the beginning, belonging to the mother's union. You know - being able to go along once a week, and meet other mums and listen to what they were saying. OK, their children weren't like mine - but being able to talk to friends was really important. You know - knowing that people were listening and sympathising, and the vicar was great. I don't know what I would have done without it." [22]

EFFECTIVE PARENTING

Effective Parenting is a primary school-based programme offered by schools and designed to support parents in the parenting role. It provides a forum to
- share experiences, fears and anxieties
- pool practical tips
- develop better understanding of relationships and behaviour and the different stages of children's development.

The aims of the programme are to bridge the divide between home and school, and to raise both parents' and children's self-esteem. An evaluation of the programme (Pugh 94) found that the training courses were effective in transferring general competence and group work skills to facilitators; that the materials used within the course were assessed as being highly appropriate and accessible by both facilitators and the majority of parents.

PIPPIN

Pippin is a growing charity, founded in 1993, which has as its main aim "Promoting Positive Early Family and Parent-Infant Relationships". All Pippin activities are evidence-based, and objectives are achieved through
- a programme for men and women on transition to parenthood
- an externally-recognised Parent-Infant Facilitator Programme for professionals and paraprofessionals
- promoting and developing collaborative interagency research and development.

Pippin's Parent-Infant Programme takes the form of 17 weekly two-hour sessions which begin in pregnancy and continue with babies in the group for three to five months post-natal. There is also a one-hour home visit just after the birth. As Pippin groups continue after the birth, they also help parents to integrate the reality of their infant and life after birth with their pre and post-natal expectations and experiences.

Evaluation of Pippin (Parr 96) found that six months post-natal, men and women on the intervention group were significantly more positive than women and men on the control group for
- emotional well-being
- satisfaction with couple relationships
- satisfaction with the parent-child relationship and parenting role
- more nurturing child-centred attitudes towards infant care.

A recent review of parenting programmes[23] found that almost all those parents taking part in the programmes felt that they had benefited.

The important role that such parenting programmes can play has been increasingly recognised both at a local and a national level. Yet, a key problem for developing parenting support remains the lack of cohesive planning at policy level and the subsequent lack of coordination at service delivery level.[24] The implications of this will be discussed alongside other policy issues later in this chapter.

Recommendation: The newly established National Family and Parenting Institute should ensure that parenting initiatives are coordinated and developed effectively. A key role for the Institute must be to ensure that there are high profile media campaigns promoting public awareness of the importance of parenting, and of the vital role parents can play in promoting children's mental health.

We warmly support the Government's recent Green Paper – *Supporting Families – A Consultation Document* and believe that its recognition of the skilled task involved in parenting and the importance of support to enable families to effectively carry out their roles is both timely and important. As the Government has recognised, family-friendly employment policies are vital if we are to enable families to promote their children's mental health.

Recommendation: The Government should give clear guidance to all employers on such issues as family-friendly working hours to enable all parents and carers to have the necessary time to spend with their children.

"I kept my feelings bottled up and still no one knows how I am feeling."

PROMOTING CHILDREN'S RESILIENCE THROUGH CHILD CARE SERVICES

An analysis of the evidence from children and young people,[25] along with research commissioned by the Foundation[26] found that
- the main supports in most children and young people's lives are family and friends
- the most common reasons for anxiety and/or depression in children and young people were connected with conflicts or loss in their family or peer relationships

- there is an enormous stigma around asking for help with emotional problems
- young people's reported mechanisms for dealing with strong negative feelings were often unsophisticated, ie either keep it in (don't talk about it or do something else) or act it out aggressively.

As we show in this Chapter, a key to ensuring that children and young people are able to access supports and help in relation to their emotional lives is the role of mainstream services in recognising the importance of, and developing expertise in, this area. Programmes which aim to promote 'emotional literacy' have an important role to play in encouraging this.

A number of studies have been carried out on the positive impact of 'emotional literacy' programmes on children. In addition to the positive impact of such schemes – children having better conflict resolution skills and being more cooperative, for example – such programmes also improve children's academic achievement scores and school performance. Such programmes are important for all children – "It's not just the kids with problems, but all kids who can benefit from these skills; these are an inoculation for life".[27]

As well as parents having an important role in 'emotionally coaching' their children, other organisations, such as child care provision, schools, out-of-school clubs and youth clubs, arts and sports organisations, have a key role to play in promoting all children's self-esteem and confidence, making them more emotionally resilient, particularly those children who are more vulnerable.

CHILD DEVELOPMENT PROJECT – OAKLAND, CALIFORNIA

This project offers a pre-packaged set of materials for schools on emotional and social skills which fit into existing courses; from stories which foster the discussion of issues, such as friendship and self-consciousness, being aware of a friend's needs, and what it feels like to be teased, through to helping teachers rethink how to discipline students who misbehave.[28]

PATHS (PARENTS AND TEACHERS HELPING STUDENTS)

Based at the University of Washington, this emotional literacy programme contains 50 lessons on different emotions, teaching the most basic, such as happiness and anger, to the youngest children and later touching on more complicated feelings, such as jealousy, pride and guilt. The emotional awareness lessons include how to monitor what they and those around them are feeling, and, most important for those prone to aggression, how to recognise when someone is actually hostile, rather than when the feelings are coming from oneself. An important part of this course is anger management, with its basic premise that "all feelings are okay to have", but some reactions are okay and others are not, and the teaching of basic tools to children to enable them to control this.[29]

Recommendation: All agencies, statutory and voluntary, working with children and young people, and particularly those working with children and young people at risk, should develop programmes of emotional and social learning within all aspects of their work.

Importance of high quality child care provision for all children

Children's access to quality day care has been clearly associated with academic and social success, but because most quality child care services have to be paid for, it is predominately children of higher income parents who are getting access to them. Whilst the need for child care has risen dramatically, with the numbers of working mothers with children aged under three having risen currently in Britain, access to quality child care is often not available – particularly for those on low income.

Important elements for high quality child care provision were identified by Mooney and Munton[30] as providing stability, consistency, sensitivity of care, which in turn are related to staff-child ratios, staff training, education and the environment. It has been argued that the quality and continuity of care is more important for children than the type of care.

"Children thrive in child care settings where they are well cared for, stimulated and secure. When children have stable and warm relationships with skilled, consistent child care staff they blossom. They are able to build strong and secure relationships with others and are helped to learn, experiment and develop their intellectual curiosity." [31]

Whilst we would not question this basic assumption, we would question whether the current segmentation of child care into distinct groups underpinned by different professional philosophies and practice is beneficial.

There are three distinct types of day care provision.

Nursery education has traditionally been provided for three and four year-olds as a free, part-time, school-based service, provided by qualified teachers, and is regulated by education legislation.

Child care for working parents is a care service for children aged up to five to cover working hours, provided by nursery nurses or unqualified care staff in a variety of private settings, including domestic settings. Finding and paying for this service has, until now, been the responsibility of parents.

Welfare care for vulnerable children or children in need is provided for young children aged up to five, referred by social workers to local authority social services or voluntary-run day nurseries or family centres, and also regulated under the terms of the Children Act (we will discuss issues relating to early interventions for vulnerable children in more detail in Chapter Three). There are also a number of local authorities, voluntary organisations and private firms that have attempted to provide nurseries which combine all three strands of nursery education, child care and welfare for vulnerable children.

The Government is currently undertaking a welcome review of all education, child care and welfare services to young children. Regrettably, they have continued to maintain the divisions already in existence between the three types of day care, even though government documents refer to 'partnership' between the different providers.

Nursery education, child care for working parents and welfare for children from vulnerable families are concerned with overlapping groups of children. Yet at present, they are differently organised, regulated, staffed and funded and, as a result, the children who attend them receive different treatment. Other European countries have arrived at more coherent solutions of these issues, either through a universal welfare system, as in the Nordic countries, or through a broader education-based system, as in France and Spain. There have also been sporadic attempts in the UK to address this, most notably in the Strathclyde Region.[32][33]

Recent research into five case study nurseries which have attempted to provide an integrated and coherent approach to nursery education, child care for working parents and welfare care for vulnerable children[34] found that the services on offer reflected the organisational starting point of the various settings, rather than a clear philosophy relating to the groups of children with whom they were working. The differences in approach between nursery education, with its assumptions that children learn best through freely-undertaken experimentation and play in a richly provided environment, and day care in which children's care and protection are of paramount importance, had an enormous impact on the range of experiences offered to the children within the different settings.

The research also highlighted the limited expectations of all the models of their relationships with parents; and vica versa, that parents did not see themselves as having any particular role in the life of the nursery. The development of 'Early Excellence Centres' to promote the best in current practice will need to address these fundamental issues.

> *"Questions of policy and practice are critical. The wider policy framework, and the organisational framework of the nursery determines daily practice; and these practices tend to persist even when policy nominally changes. In order to bring about major changes in the provision for young children, and to provide a more coherent service which provides education, child care for working parents and welfare for vulnerable children, both policy and practice have to be addressed. We need to ask very fundamental questions about who is doing what and why with young children. The situation is constantly changing, but there is so far no indication that any fundamental review is underway. The result is provision for children that is less than satisfactory."* [35]

All parents should have access to high quality child care for their children. We welcome the Government's recent review of child care. Within its proposals, the Government has clearly shown that it is committed to 'joined-up' thinking about the early years. However, there is currently no paradigm for under fives provision in this country, and failure to come to terms with this is clouding the issue for practitioners. *Sure Start* appears to be about to replicate many of the problems of existing services, and this must be addressed.

Recommendation: A coherent framework for provision for under fives, including new initiatives such as *Sure Start*, should be developed. The current demarcation between several different early years experiences, must be resolved.

Recommendation: In developing pre-school provision, the importance of children's emotional well-being, their ability to learn and to take risks should be placed centre-stage. This will require a common framework of training and practice developed for all those professionals engaged in pre-school provision to ensure that children have access to an environment that actively promotes their resilience. The variable quality of services should be addressed and standards set and monitored.

Recommendation: Within all universal pre-school provision for children, it is vital to ensure children have access to early assessment and support in relation to mental health (see Chapter Three for models of effective practice in this area). This will require

- training for all staff in the skills and knowledge to promote children's emotional well-being
- effective links between the different strands of provision envisaged by the National Child Care Strategy, *Sure Start* and National Priorities Guidance relating to child and adolescent mental health services, for example.

ROLE OF SCHOOLS IN PROMOTING CHILDREN'S MENTAL HEALTH

It is our firm belief that if we want to change things, school has to be the place to do it.

"Young people who had a good experience at school, regardless of whether they were high achievers, were more likely to belong to the 'can-do' group (those children with high self-esteem)." [36]

The activities in schools which aim to promote mental health can be divided into three broad areas:

- **strengthening individuals** – improving the emotional resilience of children; that is, how they feel about themselves and their ability to cope with stressful events, eg through circle time activities, peer support
- **strengthening communities** – increasing a sense of citizenship; that is, improving social support, social network and increasing feelings of inclusion, eg through antibullying projects
- **reducing structural barriers** – creating healthy structures; that is, the social, economic and cultural structures, eg through the development of an antidiscrimination strategy. [37]

A central way of promoting children's mental health in schools is through the recognition and implementation of social and emotional education, in all aspects of the curriculum and life of the school. Such an approach, however, would have to move against the tide of current educational policy, with its emphasis on raising standards through the requirements of the National Curriculum and league tables of schools' performance. The potentially negative impact of a narrowly focused academic definition of 'raising standards' can be seen in recent research showing evidence of increasing pupil distress in primary school[38] and of new pressures in secondary school[39] – leading to less enjoyment of learning. Teachers have reported more adverse effects than benefits on the teaching of slower learning children[40] and the evidence of 'raising standards' for those achieving five of more GCSEs at Grades A-C, being associated with falling standards for those achieving least.

Whilst we fully support the importance of academic achievement for all children, we believe that there is a pressing need to increase the emphasis of schools towards children's emotional well-being. We believe it is vital that all schools develop an ethos which encourages a shared sense of purpose, a value system that promotes high achievement for all children, and which is committed to promoting and developing social and emotional well-being. It is important that educational policy emphasises the role of schools in promoting the well-being of the 'whole child' alongside that of academic success.

"Bullies can make people upset and miserable."

Recommendation: League tables and other measures of schools performance should use a range of indicators, including
- strategies to promote children's social and emotional well-being
- the inclusion of children and young people experiencing emotional and behavioural difficulties
- creative and sporting achievements
- academic attainments.

Many schools are currently attempting, sometimes against the odds, to ensure that they do promote all of their children's well-being. There are key characteristics of schools which promote their children and young people's mental health share:
- a committed senior management team, creating a culture within the school in which the importance of trust, integrity, democracy, equality of opportunity and each child being valued regardless of their ability is seen as being vital
- a culture within the school that values teachers, lunchtime supervisors, and all those engaged in the care and supervision of the children
- clear policies regarding such vital issues as behaviour and bullying – 'whole school' behaviour policies are those which set out the range of acceptable behaviour for children, what is and what is not acceptable and the range of sanctions that will result.

Evidence to the Inquiry stressed the importance of such policies being accepted and implemented throughout the school.

Research[41] has shown that effective antibullying policies are those that are accepted and implemented at every level of the school. Schools which have whole school antibullying policies which are seen to be working appear relevant to the self-esteem of boys.[42] Evidence to the Inquiry suggested that, for antibullying policies to be effective, they should include a range of practice, including cooperative group work, quality circles in the classroom, improved playground supervision (by empowering supervisors), training vulnerable children, policies to challenge bullies and peer support services.

Recommendation: Each school, primary and secondary, should identify a mental health coordinator. The role would be to lead in the development of policies, practice, training and support aimed at promoting children's emotional well-being, as well as providing a link with primary care and child and adolescent mental health services.

Peer support

Research has demonstrated the benefits of peer support schemes in schools. These include
- the positive effects on the ethos of the school
- pupil's academic achievement
- the self-esteem of the young people involved
- the development of listening and communication skills.

Peer support systems can take a number of forms, including mentoring, befriending, conflict resolution, advocacy/advice-giving and counselling-based approaches.

As an OFSTED report has said about a school engaged in peer support, "[school] serves its pupils well, in particular in the very positive manner in which teachers and staff support the pupils by giving them strategies to manage their behaviour and promote the pupils' moral and social development and their personal welfare... This is a priority for the school and has a positive effect on the standards achieved by a significant number of pupils".[43]

"I felt unhappy when people didn't leave me alone. They called me names and beat me up. I was unhappy and scared."

A high level support and commitment to the development of peer support is important if effective models of practice are not to disappear after short-term funding and/or those individuals within the staff team committed to peer support leave.

Recommendation: Peer support schemes should be developed in all schools as part of a 'whole school' commitment to mental well-being in pupils. Funding for such schemes should be made widely available.

Personal, social and health education

It is vital in changing the ethos of schools that personal, social and health education is seen as integral to the educative process.

"The success or failure of everything we do in school is dependent on being built on a strong foundation of emotional well-being."

Within primary schools, such a policy would include such measures as 'Circle Time' for all students, and 'Circle of Friends' for those children who may be more isolated. A great deal of work has been carried out by Jenny Moseley on the impact of quality circle time within schools. Her model of a full-school implementation of quality circle time provides a useful framework for conceptualising the way in which a whole school approach to children's emotional and social well-being can be implemented.[44]

Recent research from Bristol University in a survey of the use of circle time in Wiltshire schools found that circle time can have a positive effect on the general ethos of the school, as well as on children's behaviour, social skills, self-esteem, and ability to learn.[45] Within secondary schools, personal, social and health education could play a key role in promoting young people's mental health.

"I can remember being really unhappy and it was because I was being picked on and I felt as though I were trapped."

HEXTHORPE PRIMARY SCHOOL

Hexthorpe primary school is located in a multiethnic, mainly working class area of high unemployment, and caters for over 400 pupils aged four to 11 years. In the school, an increasing number of pupils with emotional and behavioural problems seem to be struggling to cope with confusion in their personal lives. This manifests itself in low self-esteem, an inability to develop positive relationships with peers and feelings about being 'picked on' and bullied by those with whom they come into contact.

The school has developed an integrated whole school policy based on a multiagency approach in order to respond more effectively to the needs of these pupils. A combination of circle time approaches, circles of friends, the setting up of play therapy groups, and a programme aimed at the development of parenting skills helps to encourage an atmosphere of mutual trust and respect, leading to cooperative, supportive relationships between pupils, parents and staff.

Recommendation: Initiatives to promote personal, social and health education in schools should include clear guidelines as to how to develop programmes of emotional and social learning throughout the curriculum. OFSTED should develop the expertise to evaluate such programmes.

The school has a strong commitment to promoting the mental health of their pupils. The school has a slogan, "learning together, achieving together". The school has a strong pastoral system, which looks at the needs of the whole person and again includes staff as well as students. Within the school, personal, social and health education (PSHE) plays an important contribution to the mental health of students – it is not seen as being a 'tag on', and in order to increase its status and relevance the school is moving towards having teams of teachers who operate as a department.

The student-tutor relationship is given importance within the school, with the tutor being closely involved in monitoring both the academic and the 'whole person' progress of the each student. This involves regular work reviews with the student involving target settings and clear action planning for every student – enabling the tutor to focus on such aspects as learning development, and relationship issues in addition to academic progress.

The school has one school rule – to be kind to each other. This is a simple rule, yet everything else follows from it. Strategies employed at Hampstead to promote children's mental health include

- detailed information from feeder primary school teachers, and from parents on each child
- the provision of a safe haven for children between 7.30am and 7.30pm
- support teachers, for whom students are involved in the selection process
- valuing the importance of all achievements in children – not merely the academic
- clear student involvement within the school
- actively seeking to identify those students who are anxious, withdrawn, or aggressive
- an antibullying initiative, and currently looking at the introduction of peer tutoring
- the importance of having strong links with the health service.

Supports to staff

"If conditions for productive growth do not exist for teachers, they cannot create and sustain those conditions for students." [46]

It is vital that alongside supports for children and young people, schools are able to support and fully resource staff to carry out effective programmes of social and emotional literacy. This would include training and support for teachers in
- proactive classroom management
- early assessment of children experiencing problems
- working with children experiencing problems (for a further discussion of these issues see Chapter Three).

Promotion of home-school links

There has been a great deal of research showing the positive impact of effective home-school links, resulting in better individual achievement and better behaviour in school. Schools may interpret the whole concept of home-school links very differently, from positively fostering links through home-school liaison workers, through to instigating home reading programmes.

Recent research has outlined a number of examples of positive home-school links (Ball).[47] These include
- borough-wide schemes to develop links with families, such as the Parents, Children and Teachers scheme in Hackney
- the location of home-school liaison staff within an individual school.

Ball cites the National Pyramid Trust as an example of a project carrying out this work. Other initiatives to develop home-school links include setting up parents' rooms, offering parent training and support within the school, offering remedial skills programmes to parents, and providing a base for family support services, to offer parents a 'one-stop' place to find help and to facilitate collaboration between professional staff.

Westwood Park is a primary school in Park Barn, a low-density housing estate in North Guildford, serving a community severely affected by unemployment and material deprivation. A nursery class for three and four year-olds was opened in 1996 and the school has implemented a number of whole school initiatives to help children suffering from low self-esteem and poor social skills, including circle time and circle of friends approaches. Westwood Park has excellent links with agencies, such as health and social services and others, with multiprofessional meetings being a regular occurrence.

The school was aware that many parents suffer from low self-esteem and mental health problems and that these were affecting their children. The Family Assistant Project was set up to help reduce stress and anxiety among parents, to enable them to have more physical and mental energy to devote to their children, and in this way, improve the children's self-esteem.

The Family Assistant has set up many initiatives, including equipping a pleasant and welcoming parents' room at school and running classes on a range of topics, from keep-fit classes through to effective parenting. The school has a policy of carrying out home visits to all new children in the nursery class, which the Family Assistant attends. As a result of this personal contact, enabling trust to be built between the parents and the Assistant, increasing numbers of parents are joining group activities or seeking help or support over parenting issues, as well as other difficult issues in their lives, such as domestic violence and relationship problems.

Schools should be encouraged to have parent partnership policies which include means by which parents and schools can work together in both the prevention and early identification of mental health difficulties.

School as a centre for family-based services

In the USA, the model of the school as a centre for family-based services has developed in a number of disadvantaged areas. In the UK, this approach is being developed in some places. Some Children's Services Plans, for example, examine the idea of the school as a central point for service delivery to families, but, as Ball says, "as yet there is little evidence of full-scale development. However, Manchester City Council has begun an exciting pilot project in this area. We hope this and other such pilots will be fully evaluated and disseminated".[48]

This scheme aims to support children and families through schools "so that they reach a situation where their need for education and health care support approximates to the general demand without additional services". Long-term support will be available where difficulties continue, or require regular services, eg for disabled children and their families. Collaboration is taking place between a large number of agencies – health, social services, voluntary sector – and overall planning includes housing, probation and police contributions. The scheme is coordinated by a seconded headteacher.

The three primary schools chosen for the pilots have all had experience of multiagency working and have a community or parents room. Each school has its own multiagency support group, comprising the coordinator and school's head, social services team managers, education welfare officers, early years and play managers, health representatives – usually a school nurse – and representatives from the parents, voluntary sector, community police and adult education. This project is still in its early stages.[49]

In the London Borough of Hammersmith and Fulham, Section 11 funding has been used to appoint two specialist youth leaders, who work in a team with seven specialist teachers to provide support in the classroom, liaise with young people and their families, and set up individual personal development programmes in and out of school. The latter involves a combination of leadership training, outdoor pursuits, first-aid emergency training, life skills, basic education, confidence-building and job training. The team has established a strong base with schools and other education-based services. Regular meetings are held with year heads in schools, and many initiatives have emerged from collaboration with other agencies – careers guidance, social services, further education, leisure and recreation, community education, youth justice and the police. The approach has stemmed the flow of permanent exclusions of Afro-Caribbean young people in the area, and has had some unlooked-for benefits. A youth work approach has meant that some young people have been able to discuss personal problems that were previously unknown to the school. There has been a growth of understanding in the schools about the out-of-school programmes in which young people participate, and involvement in these has been acknowledged in National Records of Achievement. Youth workers have facilitated the involvement of parents in home-school work programmes and more generally in school activities.[50]

"I feel good and confident and stuff when I'm playing football and I know I'm playing well."

IMPORTANCE OF OUT-OF-SCHOOL ACTIVITIES IN PROMOTING MENTAL HEALTH

Recent research carried out in Hull found a dramatic decrease in both the range of unaccompanied activities undertaken by children and in the amount of interaction between different age groups of children and between adults and children.

Children's right to "engage in play and recreational activities" is recognised by Article 31 of the United Nations' Convention on Rights of the Child, but is becoming increasingly difficult to exercise with the decline in children's use of public play space.

Unsupervised play enables children to take risks, to think through decisions and gain increased self-confidence and greater resilience. However, as a result of parental fears, and the seeming priority given to cars over the need of children, many children's ability to play has been severely curtailed. It is important that the needs for children to play and to take certain risks and use their own initiative is recognised. Good developments include the *HomeZones* initiative, in which the usual street priorities have been reversed, and the piloting of schemes to encourage the development of safe streets for children's play by the National Play Council and Transport 2000.

With the decrease in the amount of children and young people's unsupervised play, and increasing periods of time young people spend watching television and playing computer games, the role of organisations enabling children and young people to take part in other recreational activities is increasingly important.

Young people who took part in the Foundation's *Listening to children* research talked about the importance of personal achievement for their well-being.

"More sports centres / build stuff like a club or something / bring something into Lowtown as there's nothing to do / we should have a park or shows of something, that would help keep us off the street."

"More stuff like the Islamic summer school, but longer for about three to four weeks."

"Young people need places to do up motors and smash them up and drive them about and get a good laugh. Young people take motors and stuff 'cause its a laugh and there's nothing else for them. If there were other things that gave you a buzz then you wouldn't do it."

The importance of the provision of activities, in which vulnerable young people can be enabled to engage in positive risk-taking behaviour, was highlighted by recent research[51] and evidence submitted to the Inquiry.

Initiatives announced at the end of 1997 heralded expansion for out-of-school care provision. In 1997, 2,500 out-of-school clubs provided regular services for up to 70,000 children in a variety of settings and areas. Over the next five years, levels of service are projected to increase on an unprecedented scale, providing up to one million places for children after school and during the holidays.

Research conducted at Reading University found that the key reason parents opted for out-of-school care was the play element inherent in the care.[52] Seventy per cent of respondents said they used out-of-school clubs rather than alternative forms of child care because they wanted their child to able to play with others after school or during school holidays. This supports findings of the research carried out for the Department of Health in 1990, which also found that the most significant reason parents gave for wanting their children to attend this sort of child care was to enable their children to play with others.[53]

We would strongly support this function of clubs, to facilitate children's play and to provide children with opportunities to take part in recreational activities which may otherwise be denied to them – commonly involving children in creative artwork, physical activities, music, sport and drama.[54] Outdoor adventure can help many young people to develop confidence in themselves and respect for others.

Recommendation: After and out-of-school initiatives, particularly those including arts, sports and outdoor pursuits, including outdoor adventure, should be more widely available. They should focus on developing children's emotional and social skills, and are especially important within disadvantaged areas.

THE ROLE OF SOCIAL SERVICES DEPARTMENTS IN PROMOTING CHILDREN'S MENTAL HEALTH

"The Children Act 1989 was designed to bridge the division between 'safeguarding' children and 'promoting their welfare', between 'protection' and 'prevention'. Eight years on, social services departments report that support to families is mostly confined still to children 'at risk', with few new services to other children 'in need'." [55]

As a paper from the Association of Directors of Social Services makes clear, children's services in Britain have many strengths and would be the envy of many other OECD countries, particularly the USA. But there are still evident weaknesses and areas where change needs to go further.

Many social services departments have been engaged in a great deal of refocusing work, as a direct response to the 1995 publication *Child Protection: Messages from Research*. A recent analysis by the Department of Health on expenditure of children's personal social services shows that the proportion of expenditure on children in need, but not looked after, has increased from approximately 25% in 1983 to about 40% today.[56] However, for many departments, development in this area has been seriously hampered, partly by a lack of funding.

As the Association of Directors of Social Services paper sets out, a key component of this refocusing work is an acknowledgement by local authorities that they have a key role to play in the development of services aimed at a range of children and families; from facilitating the provision of universal services to those aimed at children and families experiencing more intransigent difficulties. Whilst there have been important shifts towards the development of policy which recognises that "if more children in need can be helped to remain at home through provision of general or specific services, then the number of children in expensive out-of-home care placements will reduce".[57] Additional resourcing does need to be made available to social services departments to enable this refocusing to take place. As Acheson stressed in his recent report, "parents under stress overcome family problems when there is a wide range of sources of family support available in local communities".[58] As we will discuss in Chapter Three, it is vital that, in order to reach such families, services are effectively targeted to meet their needs, within universal mainstream services. For many parents, there remains a stigma attached to social services provision, and it remains a real challenge for many departments to turn these perceptions around. This point is especially important in relation to members of cultural minorities.

It is important that local authorities continue to develop their role in facilitating the provision of universal services, to contribute to initiatives aimed at economic and social regeneration and renewal, to embrace a wide definition and profile of children in need within their areas, and to lead the way locally in ensuring that families are encouraged to seek help and advice without fear of being labelled as having failed.

We therefore warmly welcome the Government's recent *Quality Protects* programme, with its emphasis on improved outcomes for children who receive services from social services departments, and its encouragement of social services departments within its recent consultation document, *Working Together to Safeguard Children,* to look at their child protection work in the context of services for children in need and to take a wider perspective of the needs of the child and their family.[59] It is important that a more secure framework for local government expenditure is established, in order to allow authorities to develop a more strategic approach to their expenditure priorities and thus give more attention to preventive provision "where these can be demonstrated to have long term pay-off". We welcome the stronger role for Children's Services Plans, making them a more effective instrument of corporate working within local government, and between local government and other agencies.

Recommendation: The role of local authorities in providing universal services should be strengthened, and definitions of children in need should be interpreted to include children at risk of, and experiencing, mental health problems (for a further disscussion of these issues see Chapter Three).

Whilst we welcome the recent government initiatives, especially *Sure Start* and *Quality Protects*, we are concerned that all authorities are able to benefit from the availability of pump-priming funding, and are not disadvantaged by recent changes in the way Standard Spending Assessment is calculated in relation to Children's Services.

Promoting the mental health of children and young people living away from home

Just as social services departments have a key role in developing the ability of parents to promote their children's well-being, in their role of having parental responsibility for looked-after children they have a responsibility to ensure that the well-being of those children in their care is promoted. Services for looked-after children with mental health problems will be covered in Chapter Four. Here, we are concerned to consider how the universal approach to promoting resilience in children in their families might be extended to children in the care of the local authority. So often, children being looked after miss out on the opportunities available to other children and extra effort is needed to make sure that this group are not further disadvantaged when they have already suffered adversity.

The lack of attention given to the mental health of young people in special circumstances – those who are living away from home as a result of being fostered, living in children's homes, secure accommodation, hospitals, special schools and young offender institutions, for example – is of utmost importance. Issues relating to promoting the mental health of young people within young offender institutions will be discussed within Chapter Five. An important area for future work is to examine those issues relating to promoting the mental health of children and young people within hospitals, special schools and secure accommodation.

In 1995, about 49,000 children were looked after by local authorities, whether placed in foster homes, or residential homes. The life experiences which lead to their becoming looked after mean that these young people are at far greater risk than their peers of developing mental health problems. Whilst there has been little specific research on the mental health of children and young people in foster care/looked after generally, the limited research that is available reinforces the view that they are more likely to experience mental health problems.

Research by Eastleigh Hospital found 67% of young people in residential and foster care suffered from a psychiatric disorder compared to 15% of children of the general population. In one study of young people leaving care, roughly one-sixth had long-term mental health problems, including depression, mood swings, attempted suicide, eating disorders or problems with alcohol. Over one-third had deliberately self-harmed, two-fifths had attempted suicide and three-fifths had thought about it. As the Health Select Committee on looked-after children said, "the extent to which the outcomes of looked-after children fall short of those of their peers in the general population is very worrying, and it is difficult to resist the conclusion that the system itself is underperforming. It would be a betrayal of looked-after children to suppose that significant improvements cannot be made with regard to the outcomes".

We are heartened by the priority the present government, through its *Quality Protects* programme, is placing on improving the care and support for looked-after children. The initiative, with its specific ring-fenced grants totalling some £375 million and its intention to transform the management and delivery of children's services, is welcome, as is the Government's commitment to the health education of all children, including looked-after children, as being a priority. We also welcome the Government's recognition of the particular health needs of looked-after children within *Quality Protects*, and within the National Priorities Guidance for 1999/2000 issued to the National Health Service and social service departments in September 1998.

However, within these initiatives, it is vital that the mental health of children and young people is placed centre stage. For example, whilst we welcome the priority to carry out a comprehensive health assessment of all children entering care, these must have regard to children and young people's mental health.

Recommendation: The mental health of all children entering care should be assessed, where necessary, by a psychiatrist or psychologist, and they should be offered appropriate treatment and support.

It is important that, in all aspects of support and care offered to looked-after children, attention is given to promoting their emotional well-being. For example, the importance for looked-after children of being able to maintain contact with extended families has been established. Research into young people leaving care[60]

"He used to really listen to me, almost like a mate, but not. It really helped me, feeling that someone was there, that they cared about me."

suggests that those young people who had retained family links, even when contact was not very positive, were better able to cope – "knowledge of their families, at a minimum, gave a greater symbolic certainty to their lives. Those who remained confused about their pasts found life out of care more difficult to manage – they lacked self-esteem, were less confident and assertive". Greater use of family group conferences could be a means of achieving the wider family network and achieving greater continuity in children's lives. Likewise, school links should be maintained where possible. The education needs of looked-after children must not be neglected and we welcome the attention being given to this by the Department of Health and the Department of Education and Employment.

Recommendation: Family, school and community links should be maintained and encouraged wherever appropriate, with greater emphasis on supporting families, before, during and after children being 'looked after'.

Many looked-after children are denied the opportunity to develop secure attachments, to have stable relationships and maintain a sense of continuity throughout their lives. We are very aware that children continue to be put in unnecessary multiple placements. As Childline's evidence to us highlighted, one-quarter of the 840 looked-after children who called its service had four or more placements (a few had at least 10). "Given that these are youngsters who have already experienced family loss and disruption, these are shameful statistics."

The *Quality Protects* programme has recognised the importance of this, within its first objective to "ensure that children are securely attached to carers capable of providing safe and effective care for the duration of childhood", and the National Priorities Guidance set targets for reducing multiple placements.

Recommendation: As laid out in *Quality Protects*, authorities must make every effort to ensure that children have as few placements as possible.

Recommendation: Foster parents should be given training to enable them to manage difficulties and maintain placements.

A key theme to emerge from the young people's evidence to the Inquiry was the sense of isolation felt by many who have experienced residential care. Many expressed having no one to talk to, especially an adult who might understand what they were going through. Young people reported feeling unable to use complaints procedures, for fear of not being listened to and possible retribution. Indeed, they feel stereotyped by staff as being 'in care' rather then viewed as individuals, with their own unique backgrounds and needs. The young people felt that this compounded their already low sense of self-esteem and feelings of failure.

Recommendation: Every young person in care should have an independent advocate or befriender during their entire period in care.

We believe that residential care staff could play a key role in actively helping young people to develop interests, support them educationally, as well as help them with practical matters – to act as any good parent should. However, all too often the young people presenting evidence spoke of indifference to their needs.

Where young people felt that they had developed effective relationships these were praised highly.

"You get the feeling that they're just job-worths. They don't really care about you as a person – or take an interest in you."

The development of such relationships, of social workers being the "confidants and champions of the interests of the children they look after" must be given a high priority. This will have clear training and resource implications. We welcome the Government's commitment to improve the quality of training for staff, particularly within children's homes. The development of the National Training Organisation, the General Social Care Council and the current thorough review of qualifying training for social work and residential care staff, with the establishment of conduct and practice standards, is important.

CONCLUSION

It is our belief that until we as a society really undergo a fundamental shift in our priorities, away from an increasing trend towards marginalising family life – through, for example, longer working hours, a housing policy which fails to recognise the importance of extended family networks, a taxation system which fails to prioritise the needs of families – towards that of supporting families in all their diverse forms, we will all continue to experience attitudes towards parenting which are essentially contradictory – as an increasingly difficult and demanding task requiring a whole range of skills and supports, yet as an activity which requires little time, recognition from employers or financial support.

Recommendation: A public health model for tackling children's mental health should be developed. This would mean acknowledging the importance of universal health promotion measures, including policies to reduce social inequalities. There should be a universal network of open access services linked to targeted services for those at risk.

Recommendation: Universal services should be developed that have a clear focus on promoting mental health and which are developed from a clear community empowerment perspective. Such services can be time consuming and costly to develop, but unless help and support are developed in partnership with communities enabling families to promote their children's well-being, those who are the most vulnerable will continue to fail to access help and support.

Recommendation: A high priority should be given to policies which promote families' abilities to promote their children's well-being. These would include
• a clear steer from government on the effective implementation of the 'working hours directive' for all parents and carers
• increased paid maternity and paternity leave for all parents
• an increased commitment to a shift in resources towards lower income families.

"As far as they can see, I'm just a young person in care, that's it. I'm not a great art designer." [61]

1 Utting, D (1995) *Family and Parenthood: supporting families, preventing breakdown* Joseph Rowntree Foundation, York

2 Rutter, M (1974) *Dimensions of Parenthood: some myths and suggestions* in Department of Health and Social Security *The Family in Society: dimensions of parenthood* HMSO, London

3 Einzig, H (1996) *Parenting Education and Support* chapter 16 in Bayre, R Horton, I and Bimrose, J (eds) *New Directions in Counselling* Routledge, London

4 Pugh, G, De'Ath, E and Smith, C (1994) *Confident Parents, Confident Children: Policy and practice in parenting education and support* National Children's Bureau, London

5 Kordan, L (1999) *Patterns of Parenting Support: Three Case Studies* Mental Health Foundation, London (in press)

6 Parr, M (1996) *Support for Couples in the Transition to Parenthood* unpublished PhD thesis, Department of Psychology, University of East London

7 Evidence to the Inquiry from Roger Smith

8 Lou et al (1994) *Pre-natal stressors of human life affect fetal brain development* Developmental Medicine and Child Neurology vol 36, pp826-832

9 Glover, V *Can maternal stress or anxiety in pregnancy affect the emotional development of the child?* British Journal of Psychiatry Editorial (in press)

10 Evidence to the Inquiry from Dr Vivette Glover, Queen Charlotte and Chelsea Hospital

11 Evidence to the Inquiry from Dr Mel Parr, Pippin

12 as in no 11

13 OPCS (1992) General Household Survey 1990 HMSO, London

14 Combes and Schonveld (1992) *Life will never be the same again* Health Education Authority, London Hancock, C (1994) *How effective is antenatal education?* Modern Midwife May 1994 vol 4 no 5, pp13-15

15 as in no 11

16 Rodgers, B and Pryor, J (1998) *Divorce and Separation: The Outcomes for Children* Joseph Rowntree Foundation, York

17 Rodgers, B and Pryor, J (1998) as in no 16

18 Strong, S (1997) *Unconditional Love* Mental Health Foundation, London

19 Katz, A (1994) *The family is fine... but under pressure* Sainsbury's Magazine, May 1994

20 Smith, C (1996) *Developing Parenting Programmes* National Children's Bureau, London

21 Parent in focus group

22 Parent in focus group

23 Smith, C (1996) as in no 20

24 Kordan, L (1999) as in no 5

25 O'Connell, P (1999) *Parents' evidence to the Inquiry* Mental Health Foundation, London (in press)

26 Armstrong, C Hill, M and Secker, J (1998) *Listening to Children* Mental Health Foundation, London

27 Goleman, D (1996) *Emotional Intelligence. Why it Can Matter More than IQ* Bloomsbury, London

28 Goleman, D (1996) as in no 27, p272

29 Goleman, D (1996) as in no 27, p278

30 Mooney, A and Munton, A (1997) *Research and Policy in Early Childhood Services: Time for a New Agenda* Thomas Coram Unit, London

31 Day Care Trust (1997) *Working Wonders* Briefing Paper 2

32 Penn, H and Riley, K (1992) *Managing Services for Under Fives* Longmans, London

33 Penn, H (1998) *Policy and practice in child care and education* submitted to Journal of Social Policy

34 Penn, H (1997) *Practising Excellence: The role of care and education in the early years* SSRU Institute of Education, London

35 Penn, H (1998) as in no 33

36 Buchannan, A and Katz, A (1999) *Factors Associated with High and Low Self-esteem in Boys and Girls* Mental Health Foundation, London (in press)
37 Health Education Authority (1998) *Mental Health Promotion: a quality Framework* Health Education Authority, London
38 Clarke, S (1996) *The Impact of National Curriculum Statutory Testing at Key Stages 1 and 2 on teaching and learning and the curriculum* British Journal of Curriculum and Assessment vol 1, pp12-18.
39 Ruddock, J and Harris, S (1993) *Establishing the Seriousness of Learning in the Early Years of Secondary Schooling* British Journal of Educational Psychology vol 63:2, pp322-336
40 Cox, T and Saunders, S (1994) *The Impact of the National Curriculum on the Teaching of Five Year-Olds* Falmer, London
41 Naylor, P and Cowie, H (1998) *The Effectiveness of peer support systems in challenging bullying in schools: A preliminary account of findings from a UK survey* School of Psychology and Counselling, Roehampton Institute, London
42 Buchanan, A and Katz, A (1999) as in no 36
43 Naylor, P and Cowie, H (1998) as in no 41
44 Mosley, J (1996) *Quality Circle Time in the Primary Classroom* LDA, Wisbech, Cambs
45 Dawson, N and McNess (1998) *The key themes from a survey of 'Circle Time' in Wiltshire Primary Schools* in Mosley, J *Research into the Jenny Mosley Whole School Quality Circle Time Model* All Round Success, Trowbridge
46 Sarason, S B (1993) *The Case for Change: Rethinking the preparation of educators* Jossey Bass, San Francisco
47 Ball, M (1998) *School Inclusion. The school, the family and the community* Joseph Rowntree Foundation p28/29, York

48 Ball, M (1998) as in no 47
49 Ball, M (1998) as in no 47
50 Ball, M (1998) as in no 47
51 Armstrong, C Hill, M and Secker, J (1998) as in no 26
52 Smith, F and Barker, J (1997) *Profile of Provision: The Expansion of Out of School Care* Brunel University, London
53 Meltzer, H (1994) *Day Care Services for Children: a survey carried out on behalf of the Department of Health in 1990* HMSO, London
54 Meltzer, H (1994) as in no 54
55 Association of Directors of Social Services (1997) *Investing in the Future of Children and Families, The Contribution of Personal Social Services* Association of Directors of Social Services Children and Families Committee, August 1997
56 *The Quality Protects Programme: Transforming Children's Services* DoH Circular LAC (98) 28
57 Association of Directors of Social Services (1997) as in no 55
58 Acheson, D (1998) *Independant Inquiry into Inqualities in Health report* The Stationery Office, London p74
59 *Working Together to Safeguard Children: New Government Proposals for Interagency Cooperation* (February 1998) Department of Health Consultation Paper
60 Stein, M (1997) *What Works in Leaving Care* Barnado's
61 Young person's evidence to the Inquiry

Early intervention

"You just
go round
and round
in circles
looking
for help."

INTRODUCTION

One of the most consistent messages to emerge from the evidence submitted to us is the necessity of early interventions for children at risk of developing mental health problems. The evidence shows that it is more effective to intervene early in the problem cycle and early in life. This does not preclude intervention later in the child's life – it is never too early and rarely too late to intervene. What is clear is that it is time to place prevention at the top of the nation's priorities. As the Government has recognised the importance of interventions in relation to social exclusion and offending, so the case for the effectiveness of such interventions in relation to child and adolescent mental health must be acknowledged and fully supported.

We saw in Chapter Two that first-line preventive measures need to be universally available in order to reach all those who will benefit and that they must allow access to more targeted interventions where needed. These interventions will not be overtly or solely about tackling mental health problems but will target the whole range of difficulties experienced by children that can potentially develop into more serious and troubling behaviours and problems. These initiatives should not be seen in isolation from each other nor in isolation from consideration of the broader moral, social and economic framework – "the permitting circumstances"[1]– which governments have the power to shape at national level. Although there is a dearth of cost-effectiveness studies in this area, there is enough evidence to make the case for early intervention on both effectiveness and economic grounds. We also know a great deal from the research work on risk and resilience about the types of interventions which are likely to be most effective.

There will necessarily be a debate about priorities. However complementary they may appear, prevention is different from treatment, and investment of limited public funds increasingly has to choose between the two. It is our belief that specialist mental health services for children and adolescents will always be needed and are currently shamefully underfunded and resourced. At the same time, as many children, young people and their parents as possible should be able to receive help and support within mainstream services, before their difficulties develop into more severe and intractable problems.

This Chapter will explore in more detail issues of early interventions. We know that "interventions are most effective if they target more than one level at a time".[2] As with parenting education and support generally, interventions for those at risk have to be available at key transition points in the life of families, notably the period around birth, the pre-school period, and the transition to and from school. However, one-off educative or skills-based interventions for families, the 'inoculation' model, are of limited effectiveness. The challenge, therefore, is for services to be available, accessible and acceptable to families, children and young people on a continuing basis and for them to reach those who are most at risk and who are often those most difficult to engage – the Inverse Care Law.

This Chapter will look at what is known about the risk factors for children within their families and what interventions are effective around the time of birth and during the early years. Pre-school compensatory programmes and early interventions in schools show the importance of interventions targeted both at the parents and the child. The contribution of agencies, such as primary health care, will be examined and the implications of early intervention ideas for future developments will be drawn out.

EARLY INTERVENTIONS FOR FAMILIES

What is known about risk factors in families

The great majority of families, whatever the nature of the parents' own problems, provide protection and effective stimulus to promote the positive development of their children. It is when external circumstances combine with adverse family circumstances that negative developmental processes in the child are reinforced rather than prevented. For example, families living in particular geographical locations, especially inner city locations with higher than average concentrations of risk, such as poor housing and family poverty, will be particularly at risk if there are also poor parental relationships, family violence, or the child has particular characteristics or special needs.

Social factors

Low socioeconomic status is a risk factor for a wide range of health, cognitive and behavioural problems in early childhood. Fonagy[3] has argued that children from low socioeconomic backgrounds are in 'double jeopardy' as they are not only exposed more frequently to risk factors but experience more serious consequences from these risks.[4] People living in poverty have increased vulnerability to negative life events, such as single parenthood, social isolation, and loss of employment which can in turn impact both directly and indirectly on parents' relationships with their children. For example, it may reduce their ability to parent well or it may mean that buying toys and books for their children is not a possibility.

Family characteristics

The quality of parental relationships and the availability of social supports have been identified as key factors affecting parenting competence.[5] Numerous studies have linked the quality of the parents' relationship to infant functioning. Conflict has been shown to predict 'abnormal' infant behaviour and conduct problems in toddlers.[6] Studies comparing the effect of family instability (loss of a parent as a result of divorce or death) and marital conflict have consistently found marital conflict to have the greater negative influence.[7] Where supportive parental relationships do not exist, then social support is very important. Thus, levels of clinical depression amongst mothers have been shown to be highest where there is a poor marriage, poor social support and a reported poor relationship with their own mother, alongside poor housing and environment.[8] The increased risk to children from having parents with mental health problems is not related directly to their parents' illness or specific symptomatology, but to associated problems in the family.

"If my son had received help when he was five years old, instead of when he was 15, I am sure he would have benefited and his confidence would not have been so badly damaged."

Abundant evidence exists that a coercive, hostile, critical and punitive parenting style is associated with a substantially increased risk of antisocial behaviour in the child.[9] It is also clear that certain groups of parents are more at risk of using coercive styles of parenting due to their own histories of being parented and current stresses. For example, Patterson[10] found that maternal stress from negative life experiences, including financial burdens, was a significant contributor to coercive disciplining strategies, which in turn predicted antisocial behaviour in the child. At the most severe end of poor parenting, maltreatment, ie severe neglect, physical, emotional or sexual abuse, is one of the most potent risk factors for children. It has been shown that maltreatment undermines the capacity for bonding and intimate relationships, which may, in turn, lead to aggression and/or social withdrawal, and undermine the child's ability to make appropriate attributions about human behaviour.

INTERVENTIONS FOCUSED ON FAMILIES

An effective case has been made for early intervention to prevent social exclusion and youth offending and the Government has recently made a commitment to early intervention, particularly in relation to the important *Sure Start* initiative. As we have seen, many of the factors relating to early childhood mental health problems and factors leading to social exclusion and antisocial behaviour overlap. And whilst not all mental health problems in children and young people are open to preventive early childhood intervention, eg depression, there is a clear case to be made for effective early interventions for those problems that can be dealt with.

- 20% of children and adolescents experience psychological problems – with 10 to 12% experiencing mental health problems which significantly impact on their lives.
- The poor long-term outcome of untreated impairment, which has always been accepted for pervasive development disorders and schizophrenia, is now increasingly recognised for disruptive behaviour problems.[11]
- Even those emotional disorders of childhood which were traditionally thought to remit spontaneously have been found to have poor recovery rates, mostly around 50%.[12]
- Early mental health problems in children can persist to later childhood. A review[13] showed that about two-thirds of three year-olds who showed significant disturbance still had difficulties when assessed at age eight or 12. This is particularly true of the disorders which are of greatest cost and concern to the wider society, eg violent conduct disorder.[14]

Interventions around the time of the child's birth

We have seen that universal support to families around the birth of a child has beneficial effects (Chapter Two) and enables the identification of mothers at risk. There are a number of examples of effective programmes focused on mothers at risk.

COMMUNITY MOTHERS' PROGRAMME – DUBLIN, IRELAND

This programme involved the recruitment and support of up to 20 "community mothers" by specially appointed Programme Coordinators or Family Development Nurses. The areas chosen for the intervention were those that were disadvantaged, based on housing type, social class, education and employment and in which there were a large number of births.

The "community mothers" were trained over approximately six hours in their own home, and were in turn each responsible for between five and 15 first-time mothers. The community mothers visited the target mothers at least monthly for the first year of their child's life and provided a long visit discussing the child's development and the mothers input in a way tailored to individual family circumstances. A control group received standard support from the public health nurse.

A large proportion (89%) of the first-time mothers completed the study. Those children who had been part of the study were more likely to have received all of their primary immunisations, to have been read to daily, to have played more cognitive games and were exposed to more nursery rhymes. Their weaning and diet were judged to be more appropriate. The mothers also reported a better diet and at the end of the study were less likely to report being tired, feeling miserable or wanting to stay indoors.

This programme was not delivered by professionals but by experienced mothers living in the same communities. These mothers were expected to share their experiences and raise the self-esteem and confidence of the young mothers in parenting. These results are seen to support a model of empowerment, and to be sound, practical and effective.[15]

SOCIAL SUPPORT AND PREGNANCY OUTCOME (SSPO)[16]

This study demonstrated the effectiveness, appropriateness and safety of a social support intervention in 'high risk' pregnancy provided by midwives. A total of 509 women with history of low birth-weight were randomised to receive either social support intervention in pregnancy in addition to standard antenatal care or standard antenatal care only.

Social support was given by four midwives in the form of 24-hour contact telephone numbers and a programme of home visits. The midwives provided a listening service for women to discuss any topic of concern to them, gave practical information and advice when asked, made referrals to other health professionals and welfare agencies as appropriate, and collected social and medical information. The number of hospital antenatal clinic visits was the same in the two groups, but more women in the control group (52%) than in the intervention group (41%) were admitted to hospital in pregnancy. Women's attitudes to the social support intervention were found to be very positive – 80% of those who filled in the post-natal questionnaire singled out as important the fact that the midwife listened. As follow-up has continued, differences between the two groups has been maintained, with more positive results in the intervention group. At seven years, there were fewer behavioural problems amongst the children and less anxiety among the mothers in the intervention group.

Early intervention for women experiencing post-natal depression

The impact of post-natal depression on children's cognitive and emotional development has been well documented. Maternal depression in infancy is associated with long-term effects on the child's physical and psychological health, behaviour and academic performance.[17] Research has shown that infants of post-nataly depressed mothers were more insecurely attached to their mothers, performed worse on object concept tasks and showed mild behavioural difficulties.[18] The impact of post-natal depression appears to have a particularly adverse impact on male infants in terms of lower IQ and less secure attachments. Later, teachers reported that half of the study children had difficulties and more problematic relationships than other children.[19]

Between 10 and 15% of women experience episodes of major depressive disorder in the weeks and months following child-birth.[20] In relation to post-natal depression, there are major concerns:
• the lack of effective pre-birth screening for at risk mothers
• the lack of effective primary care input for mothers experiencing post-natal depression
• the lack of specialist services for those mothers needing them
• lack of coordination between adult and child services.[21]

There are already highly effective structures in place, delivered by midwives and health visitors, to monitor the general progress of pregnant and postpartum women and their babies. Such a structure could be effectively utilised, at little additional cost, for the identification of those at risk, the early detection and speedy treatment of postpartum illness, and the screening at post-natal examination for post-natal illness. This could be done by routinely enquiring about well-being and mental health or, preferably, by the use of the Edinburgh Post-natal Depression Scale. This scale has been used successfully by trained health visitors who can screen women during a home visit 10 weeks after the birth.[22] Research evidence suggests that various forms of home support or home visiting during pregnancy improves the mental well-being of women and children.[23] Trials also indicate that continuous support for women during labour (from friends or volunteer labour companions) can reduce post-natal depression and raise self-esteem.[24] A study in London found that special antenatal groups for potentially vulnerable women halved the incidence of post-natal depression. An important aspect of these groups was that they provided women with peer support, as well as post-natal help.[25]

The desirability of increasing the role of health visitors in the treatment of post-natal depression was also recommended by Murray in her evidence to the Inquiry. Health visitors, trained in delivering brief psychological treatments (counselling, cognitive behavioural therapy), have been shown to be effective in relieving post-natal depression within a period of two months in a great majority of cases.[26] Again, these treatments have a significant benefit in reducing levels of behavioural disturbance in the infant.

Recommendation: Health visitors should screen all new mothers for post-natal illness and be trained in short-term interventions for post-natal depression.

It is important that midwives and health visitors are able to work closely together. Evidence stressed that current professional boundaries can get in the way of delivering an effective service for women. We also heard examples of midwives and health visitors working effectively together – providing an important continuum of care for a young family.

Recommendation: It is important that structured programmes of home visiting are developed for families at risk. Such programmes should work in partnership with parents, offering practical support and help, and engage in 'active listening'. They should be able to offer short-term therapeutic interventions for those families displaying early problems, to encourage parents to develop other social supports and to be able to refer those parents or children who require it onto more specialist provision.

Recommendation: The training of all health visitors and midwives must give attention to mental health issues. Specialist training and supervision from mental health specialists should be available for health visitors to work with parents and children experiencing mental health problems.

We are concerned that the ability of health visitors to provide services for all parents is compromised when they are based in individual practices with no wider strategic influence. As primary commissioning groups become established, there must be sufficient funding and support to ensure that primary care and community-based professionals are able to deliver support and services for children and families experiencing mental health problems.

Services for severely depressed mothers and babies

An area of particular concern is the general lack of specialist knowledge about working with mothers with mental health problems and their newborn babies. A further problem is that those trained in adult mental health, whether psychiatrists, social workers or nursing staff looking after the mother, are unlikely to have been trained in the needs of babies and children, and vice versa. This is further exacerbated because the links between adult mental health services and child mental health and social worker/midwifery services are weak.

The risk for women with a previous history of affective psychosis of developing mental illness post-birth is thought to be between 1:3 and 1:2.[27] Such a level of risk indicates the importance of effective work and planning with such women – enabling both professionals and family to plan for necessary support for both parent and child.

ST MICHAEL'S FELLOWSHIP

St Michael's Fellowship is a voluntary organisation which runs four residential family assessment units, one working with adolescent mothers, one with families where parents have drug/alcohol dependencies and two where there may be serious child abuse and/or parents have learning difficulties, or mental health problems. Families are referred to St Michael's by local authority social service departments in London and the Home Counties. The organisation also provides three-month assessments of a parent's ability and potential to meet the needs of their child(ren). Each house is staffed by a skilled team offering 24-hour cover. Families on admission to St Michael's are responsible for their children and are expected to perform the basic tasks of daily living, eg personal care and preparation of basic meals. Often, families where the parent has a mental health problem are referred straight from hospital. They tend to be lone mothers with very little or no support from a partner or extended family. They generally come with very young babies where their mental illness has raised concern amongst social workers about their ability to meet their child's needs or there is a previous history where children have been removed.

In her submission to us, the Director of St Michael's suggested that the following issues need to be addressed:
- the importance of mothers being encouraged to feed, bathe and clothe their babies whilst in hospital
- the importance of observing whether the effects of medication is impacting on the parent's ability to care for their child
- developing a network of support with the parent to meet their needs on discharge to the community, one person to be assigned a coordinating role with responsibility for ensuring that the community psychiatric nurse and the health visitor visit, and that doctors appointments, etc are kept.

It is important that the needs of both mothers who are severely depressed and those of their babies are met. Currently, too many women are still being placed inappropriately on general psychiatric wards, which are not geared-up to meeting the needs of women and their babies. The development of specific, specially-staffed psychiatric mother and baby units in each area could help to resolve many of the problems.

Oates[28] describes the distinctive characteristics of such a service as being
- able to provide in-patient facilities for mothers and babies
- staffed by a multidisciplinary team, whose members will need to possess special skills and understanding
- to be able to respond rapidly to over a third of all patients referred, seeing them either at home or on the post-natal wards – the majority of the patients will be seriously mentally ill, at least twice as many as amongst new referrals to general psychiatric services, and are three times more likely to be seen in an emergency
- the team must include community psychiatric nurses with the ability to cope with severely ill women at home, many of whom have older children
- the team will have to liaise not only with general practitioners and health visitors, but also obstetric services, child psychiatrists and social services.[29]

The lack of joint responsibility and planning for seriously ill mothers and their babies, appropriate in-patient and community-based service provision, and lack of appropriate training for professionals working in this area were of serious concern.

Recommendation: Each area needs to develop in-patient facilities for women who are severely mentally ill and their newborn babies, staffed by multidisciplinary teams, whose members will need to possess special skills and understanding.

Recommendation: It is important that better understanding and closer cooperation between adult and children's services is developed. Whilst we believe that it is appropriate for child and adolescent mental health services to be located within children's services, such a demarcation could lead to an increasing gulf between children's and adult's services. Thus we would want to see developed
- specialist posts based in social services departments, child and adolescent mental health services and adult psychiatry which are specifically linked to maternity and post-natal services
- agreements between health and social services to focus resources jointly for mentally ill parents.

It is not only mothers who are at risk of depression and other mental health problems. The problem of depressed fathers has received less attention, as indeed has the role of fathers within the family generally. Children in families where there is domestic violence, parents with personality disorders and parents with drug and alcohol problems are at great risk of developing mental health problems.

As the example of St Michael's shows, it is not enough to extend statutory services important though that is. It is also essential that those agencies currently engaged in innovative work within the community are appropriately funded to continue and develop this work further. We would particularly want to see the funding of pilot projects, and the further evaluation of what works.

Interventions for families with young children

Research has shown that early intervention programmes focused on first-time mothers are particularly effective because of their acknowledgement of the need for social support and child rearing assistance.

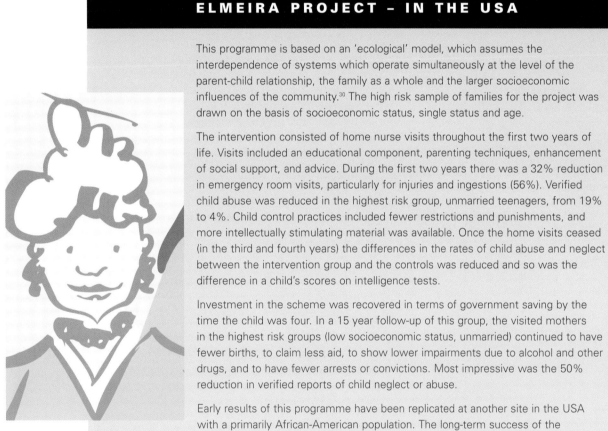

ELMEIRA PROJECT – IN THE USA

This programme is based on an 'ecological' model, which assumes the interdependence of systems which operate simultaneously at the level of the parent-child relationship, the family as a whole and the larger socioeconomic influences of the community.[30] The high risk sample of families for the project was drawn on the basis of socioeconomic status, single status and age.

The intervention consisted of home nurse visits throughout the first two years of life. Visits included an educational component, parenting techniques, enhancement of social support, and advice. During the first two years there was a 32% reduction in emergency room visits, particularly for injuries and ingestions (56%). Verified child abuse was reduced in the highest risk group, unmarried teenagers, from 19% to 4%. Child control practices included fewer restrictions and punishments, and more intellectually stimulating material was available. Once the home visits ceased (in the third and fourth years) the differences in the rates of child abuse and neglect between the intervention group and the controls was reduced and so was the difference in a child's scores on intelligence tests.

Investment in the scheme was recovered in terms of government saving by the time the child was four. In a 15 year follow-up of this group, the visited mothers in the highest risk groups (low socioeconomic status, unmarried) continued to have fewer births, to claim less aid, to show lower impairments due to alcohol and other drugs, and to have fewer arrests or convictions. Most impressive was the 50% reduction in verified reports of child neglect or abuse.

Early results of this programme have been replicated at another site in the USA with a primarily African-American population. The long-term success of the programme was associated with structural change in the mother's life, particularly relating to a delay in second pregnancy, and the provision and good take-up of pre-school facilities.

It has been argued[31] that only a minority of programmes for first-time mothers are effective, but those which are have important and widespread benefits, including significant economic ones. It appears to be the structured programmes accompanying home visiting which produce the beneficial outcomes, rather than the home visiting itself.

A study in Bristol showed similar benefits.

This programme offers monthly support visits by specially trained health visitors, who use semistructured methods and provide parents with strategies for tackling child care and child rearing issues. Some programme visiting is also undertaken with parents of two or more children who face particular problems in coping with their children. The fundamental goal of the programme is to support parents in their task, along with offering them support in relation to their own health and well-being. Following a simple protocol, parents and health visitors explore issues such as health, development, diet and self-esteem. Parents are encouraged to set themselves developmental, dietary, health and other tasks to carry out with their children in the month following the visit.

Evaluation has indicated that, despite programme families being generally more disadvantaged than non-programme families, on almost every major outcome programme families scored more highly than non-programme families.[33]

Interventions for families of children showing early behaviour problems

It has been argued that, out of all the problems experienced by children, it is conduct disorder which should be the key target of early intervention. Conduct disorder

- is the most common reason for referral to mental health services for boys
- is resistant to treatment, particularly in adolescence
- should become increasingly identifiable in its early stages
- has a more serious outcome the earlier the onset
- early preventive interventions may be effective in modifying trajectories and thus interrupt the course towards chronic antisocial behaviour.

We know from research that interventions targeting key risk and resilience factors can be effective. Programmes combining family support with early education have prevented delinquency through their impact on multiple risk factors.

There has been a strong emphasis in recent years on interventions designed to improve the parenting skills of parents of children with behaviour problems. Such work is consistent with research that "family functioning rather than family structure has the greatest impact upon outcomes for children".[34] In Barlow's systematic review of parenting programmes working in this field, the findings were largely positive, showing that group-based parenting programmes did have an impact on improving the behaviour of young children.

In following up the children after time, results showed the effects of parent training programmes on children's behaviour was enduring, but that, in a number of cases, as many as 50% of parents continued to experience problems with children's behaviour. These families were characterised by single parent family status, increased maternal depression, lower social class status and family history of alcoholism and drug abuse.

However, the work of Webster-Stratton in the USA shows that, for children with clinically defined behaviour problems from high-risk backgrounds, videotape modelling can be effective in changing children's behaviour. Research into the cost-effectiveness of this work in Britain is currently being carried out by Scott at the Maudsley (see Chapter One).

Parenting courses are a useful tool within a broad range of potential supports for families, particularly where accurate assessments have been made by the parents themselves or others of the need for information or skills training.[35] But if parenting courses are used as stand-alone interventions, they are unlikely to have long-lasting effects. Families with long-standing and complex problems are likely to require complex packages of long-term support. A range of work showing particular promise is that in which parent education is carried out alongside interventions with the child in school[36] (see *C'mon Everybody*, Chapter Three).

Early compensatory pre-school interventions

There is clear evidence that "programmes combining direct developmental services to young children with parent support and education hold the most promise of improved long-term child development outcomes."[37] Pre-school programmes to improve the cognitive and social development of disadvantaged children from deprived backgrounds have a major role to play in developing children's resilience. The evaluation of the Perry Pre-school/*High Scope* programme in the USA has demonstrated long-term benefits and cost-effectiveness.

High Scope shares many of the elements of other good quality pre-school programmes, but what is seen to be particularly important within this approach are

- the active learning curriculum – it has been suggested that it is the active learning component that results in children acquiring long-lasting academic, social and cognitive gains
- the input of trained staff
- active parent participation – "The best protection for children apparently in the long-term is parental interest in, and enthusiasm for, their education".

Evidence suggests that participation in the programme resulted in a reduced likelihood of early school failure and placement in special education and generally a positive attitude towards school. 'School commitment' is also shown to be protective against later risk of maladjustment and delinquency.[38]

When the children reached 27 they showed

- significantly higher monthly earnings (29% vs 7% earning $2000 or more per month)
- significantly higher level of schooling completed (71% vs 54% 1st grade or higher)
- significantly lower percentage receiving social services at some time in the past 10 years (59% vs 80%)

CAROLINA ABECEDARIAN PROGRAMME

A further example of an extensive preventive programme providing services directly to children is the Carolina Abecedarian programme. This, whilst targeted at children, also had an indirect benefit to mothers, as the programme was based in a day care setting, enabling the mothers to seek work if they wanted. The criteria for selection onto the programme were family risk factors, children being selected on the basis of the mothers being young (17 or less), with backgrounds characterised by low education, low income and, in some cases, learning difficulties or mental health problems.

Random assignment to a high quality day care setting by the age of three months or to a no-intervention group took place. The day care programme had a systematic curriculum, high staff to child ratio, and it provided free medical care and free transport. The findings of the study were that those children thought to be at greatest risk, showed equal or greater gains than the groups as a whole. This data corresponds with other findings that when multiple risk factors are involved it may be more effective to intervene directly with the child rather than the parent.[39]

The Abecedarian project continued beyond the pre-school period, with a second phase of intervention taking place when the children entered elementary school. This study also supports the view that a 'dose' model for preventative work may be more relevant than an 'inoculation model', since continued interventions led to increasing differences between those who had experienced the intervention and those who had not, or who had been in pre-school centres, but not followed up in school.[40]

- significantly fewer arrests (7% vs 35% with five or more) including arrests for crimes of drug-taking.

Recommendation: The Government has clearly demonstrated its commitment to the development of pre-school education for all three to four year-olds. This commitment should be extended to the provision of high quality appropriate pre-school education for all children in areas of high deprivation.

Characteristics of successful early interventions

Perhaps the most clinically significant findings of the early intervention studies have been from those which demonstrated a reduction of childhood physical and sexual abuse and neglect. A number of home visit studies offer evidence that physical maltreatment and neglect can be prevented, although not all studies demonstrate significant benefit.[41] However, as Fonagy[42] has argued, "Beyond the humanitarian significance of the findings, in view of the well-documented and serious sequelae of childhood maltreatment,[43] these findings are of the utmost importance to preventive mental health care".

The enthusiasm for early interventions must be tempered by an understanding of their limitations. It is unfortunately often those in greatest need who decline the invitation to take part. The challenge is, therefore, to ensure that interventions are acceptable and appropriate to those most in need. Similarly, the results of early interventions are generally poorer with what appear to be more high-risk groups. There are, nonetheless, features of successful programmes on which interventions can be based. Non-specific, poorly structured treatments, such as generic counselling, non-focused dynamic therapy and a variety of experiential therapies, are unlikely to be effective.

Evidence clearly suggests that short-term interventions with those individuals or families experiencing multiple problems also tend to be ineffective.

Recommendation: Preventive interventions must begin early, be long-term and be directed at risk factors, addressing those disorders where 'at risk' populations have been identified by research. Programmes must be long-term to have lasting effects and be evaluated.

There is also evidence that not only the type of intervention, but the manner and location of its delivery, affect its outcomes. The following factors are those which are common to interventions which have been effective or have shown promise.

Community participation – "Interventions which actively involve local people can provide a solid basis upon which to build a spectrum of family support services. Community projects may not be able to provide the professional support which some families need, but they can provide a valuable role in referring families on to other forms of support." [44]

Local interventions – If interventions are targeted at particular communities identified as being at risk, such targeting has to be sensitively handled so as to minimise the possibility of stigmatisation. Services targeted on communities are more likely to be
- accessible by local transport systems
- sensitive to the social and cultural diversity of the local community
- more able to work in partnership
- able to draw on the energy and commitment of key charismatic individuals
- able to match needs with interventions.

As evidence from Barnardos makes clear, "Policy implications arising from promising services with a mental health focus concern the location where they should be delivered... such services should be embedded in a system of universal provision for young children with an emphasis on early years services in health and education".[45] In an effort to move away from the very differently demarcated forms of child care, with their concurrent levels of stigmatisation, pre-school services should be promoted as a positive resource for all parents according to their needs, and as a mechanism for promoting the well-being of children.

Such location of initial interventions within mainstream services does not preclude the targeting of services across communities, nor the development of specialist services, which respond to the many complex needs that families can present. Indeed, good provision offers the chance to build supportive networks in the community which will have further protective effects.

The lack of effective assessment of needs was one of the key messages in parents' evidence to us. Many parents felt that they
• had had to wait too long for their child's needs to be assessed
• were often given contradictory messages relating to the assessment process and outcome from an assessment, depending on which professional group had carried it out
• often lacked appropriate help, or felt they were given inappropriate services for themselves and their child.

What is clear is that, in the views of professionals, parents and young people, current services fall well short in terms of availability, in the spread of expertise and in the manner and style of delivery.

> *"A fundamental shift is required if children's life chances are to be seen as both a community and a governmental responsibility requiring the deployment and investment of national and local resources."* [46]

We welcome the recent announcement by government of the *Sure Start* initiative. This initiative, comprising an additional £540 million which will be made available over three years, is aimed at "the needs of young children and their families in areas of greatest need".

The availability of funding, to enable local partnerships to deliver support services, including family support, child care, health care, early learning and play, will provide an important focus for the development of early interventions for families experiencing difficulties and those children at increased risk of developing mental health problems within more mainstream settings.

Recommendation: Initiatives such as *Sure Start* must be backed by stable long-term funding. Without such long-term investment we fear that many extremely positive interventions will collapse after their initial pump-priming funding has ended. Interventions should also be evaluated.

Recommendation: The prevention of serious disturbance needs long-term and intensive commitment. There must be a commitment at both local and national level, to the development of early intervention services for older children, three plus, at risk of developing/who have developed mental health problems. Such a programme will require resourcing, in addition to that made available for *Sure Start*, *Quality Protects* and the National Priorities Guidance in relation to children's mental health.

"I have always known there was a problem from the time he was small ... he was not diagnosed with dyslexia until he was 11. I believe the lack of confidence as a result of this has led to his mental problems."

"A good school has made all the difference – professionals know what to do and their expertise and knowledge is second to none." [47]

EARLY INTERVENTIONS IN SCHOOLS

"There needs to be more awareness in schools, particularly, as to what to look for in children with mental health problems." [48]

One of our main conclusions is that the most effective means of improving the mental health of children and adolescents is by improving the ability of mainstream agencies to deliver help and support before problems become intractable. This conclusion contains an enormous challenge. A key aspect of effective early interventions for children is that they take place where children are most likely to present – child care settings, schools, and general practitioner surgeries – and that those working with children in these settings should receive the necessary skills and support, on both a personal and a structural level, to do this.

Schools have a vital role to play in early interventions for children experiencing mental health problems. Children with special education needs must be included in local education authorities' proposals for raising educational standards, and it is our view that this should include specific mention of children with mental health problems. We believe that, given appropriate training, leadership, funding and governmental support, schools could play a key role in ensuring that children and young people on first displaying mental health problems could gain access to important help at a community level.

"After six years there is still no appropriate educational help. This has caused so much damage to our child and so much stress to us."

A positive school experience can have a beneficial, protective effect for vulnerable children. Negative experiences lead to greatly increased risk. Schools can ensure that children can gain access to appropriate help and support before their problems become entrenched. Those examples of practice that have been evaluated suggest that such work can be effectively carried out by those working from either an educational or social services perspective. Support for children with more intractable problems would come from health professionals.

We are not suggesting that teachers should 'double up' as mental health workers, but that attention to children and young people's mental health should be an integral concern of all those working with children. Enabling staff to develop the skills to prevent problems from developing in the classroom and the playground, and ensuring that they have access to appropriate help and support within a school setting, could be an effective way of delivering non-stigmatising services to many children and young people. The early identification of difficulties was one of the key issues in the evidence to the Inquiry, as was the need to be able to offer a flexible interagency response.

Recommendation: All teachers within mainstream schools should have continuing training on child development issues, an understanding of the sources of mental health difficulties, and straight forward interventions, ie behaviour management techniques.

Within the education field, considerable work has been carried out in relation to effective practice for children experiencing emotional and behavioural problems. It is not the role of this report to reexamine all of this. We do, however, want to reaffirm a number of key principles in relation to early interventions for children experiencing mental health problems.

Children with emotional and behavioural difficulties

"Emotional and behavioural difficulties may show through withdrawn, depressive, aggressive or self-injurious tendencies. There may be one or more causes. Family environments or physical sensory impairments may be associated. Children with emotional and behavioural difficulties... always have special educational needs." [49]

Children experiencing problems (and predominately externalising problems) in schools have tended to be defined as having emotional and behavioural difficulties. Local education authorities now have to have in place a statement of their arrangements for dealing with pupils who have behavioural difficulties (Behaviour Support Plans) and should be able to use this to describe how they will relate to other agencies, such as child and adolescent mental health services and social services, in providing help for children with mental health difficulties.

Educational policies, which are focusing resources and strategies predominantly on those children defined as having emotional and behavioural difficulties, risk overlooking a great many children experiencing real difficulties, but not necessarily causing the school any problem. Those children whose difficulties are less obvious and cause less 'trouble' to others may not fit the description of emotional and behavioural difficulties, and may not therefore access the help they need. An overemphasis on emotional and behavioural difficulties may disadvantage those with more internalising disorders, eg depression, eating disorders, anxiety. It may also lead to those with attention deficit hyperactivity disorder or other serious disorders failing to get the health input they need because their needs are defined within the educational sphere. There is a need to overcome the differences in approach between the different agencies – education, health, social services – which manifest themselves in various approaches to assessment and intervention and even different terminology being used to describe the same child and their problems.

These differences are compounded by the requirements of law, which give a different focus to what are regarded as severe or serious problems in the education, health and social service sector. For example, under the 1996 Education Act, a child with serious problems is to be defined by means of a statement of special educational needs. However, different local authorities have applied different criteria in assessing whether a child is eligible for a statement. These criteria have been influenced by the availability of resources rather than perceptions about the seriousness of problems or a comprehensive assessment of the needs of the child. [50]

With the development of Behaviour Support Plans and an emphasis on the ethos of schools, there is a move to embrace a more holistic approach to children's development. However, the statementing approach in schools is currently experienced, especially by parents and children, as complicated, over-lengthy and of little tangible benefit (parents' evidence). It was felt by parents that more could be achieved by freeing up educational psychologists' time to be spent in schools working therapeutically with individual children, rather than on bureaucratic processes resulting in little effective intervention.

The HAS report [51] found that school psychology services were largely used to support or assess statements of special educational needs – of which only about one in five were for children with emotional and behavioural problems. Mental health professionals interviewed, who said that they had provided support for schools in the past, reported that health commissioners were no longer prepared to fund activity to help teachers deal with troubled or troublesome pupils. [52]

"We had to jump through so many hoops to get a statement, and then when we succeeded it didn't seem to make any difference, there still wasn't any real help for him."

There is a need for systematic, coordinated, multidisciplinary and practical help for children in schools, including specialist input from child and adolescent mental health services and educational psychology services. Schools offer an important access point for assessment and intervention as part of a whole school framework for promoting the mental health of all children.

Recommendation: The focus of the role of educational psychologists should shift away from a focus on the statementing process, towards offering schools advice on interventions, programme planning/supervision and direct therapeutic interventions with the child/family in relation to mental health. In order for educational psychologists to deliver this, there must be an increase in their numbers. Currently, many local authority psychology services are operating below Warnock (1981) staffing levels of 1:3,000. Many are still operating below the level of 1:5,000 – this target as a minimum must be met.

Children who are at risk of exclusion from school

The number of school exclusions has risen dramatically, particularly from primary schools. Statistics for 1995/6 show that there were 12,500 permanent exclusions from primary, secondary and special schools, an increase of 13% over the previous year. Of these, 1,400 (13%) were from primary school, an increase of over 18% over the previous year.[53]

Research into the rise of primary exclusions indicated that the majority of children investigated had suffered significant and multiple stresses in their lives. "The most common issues were breakdown in the relationship of birth parents, which was present in 33 cases (87%); the evidence of special educational needs, found also in 33 cases (87%); in 25 cases (66%) there was involvement of social services with the family and, of these, 17 children (45%) had spent time 'looked after' by the local authority; and in 23 cases (60%) children had been through multiple moves and disruption, resulting in changes of school as well as residence".[54]

As with early interventions for families, research has demonstrated that effective interventions within school are those which are durable over time, are multicomponent and multilevel interventions.[55] Early interventions which are not firmly located within a supportive wider school ethos, which do not take into account the multiple risk factors likely to be present for many children and young people, and which fail to take into account aspects of the child's functioning outside the school, are likely to be ineffective.

This finding can be clearly demonstrated in relation to children at risk of school exclusion. The negative impact of school exclusion and lack of school attendance has been clearly demonstrated to increase risk of antisocial behaviour and involvement in youth crime. It also has a potential impact in relation to children's mental health. As Carl Parsons' evidence to the Inquiry stated, "exclusion is a blow, socially, psychologically and emotionally – it is vital that elements from health are brought in to collaborate in enterprises to manage these children and help them manage their behaviour".

The overrepresentation of African-Caribbean students is a major concern; they account for 8% of permanent school exclusions, whilst they make up only 2% of the total school population. Kurtz questions whether the disproportionate numbers of African-Caribbean pupils being excluded is because "behaviours in young people from different social, racial and cultural backgrounds are liable to be interpreted and treated differently".[56]

The multidimensional nature of positive practice relating to children at risk of exclusion can be demonstrated by The Lynx Room.

THE LYNX ROOM –
an in-school support centre, Alexandra Primary School, Haringey

Alexandra Primary is an inner city school amalgamated in January 96. It has an intake which includes a significant number of families experiencing considerable difficulties, such as asylum seekers and refugees. It has a high pupil turnover and admits a large number of casual transfers. When the centre was first established using GEST funding there was also a high rate of exclusion.

The centre was set up primarily to work with pupils at risk of exclusion. It was intended to

* enable the school to develop a range of strategies to meet the needs of pupils with behavioural difficulties
* enable the school to develop early identification procedures for pupils with behavioural difficulties
* enable all staff to be involved in the overall planning of the centre
* provide a model which could be repeated in other schools
* support pupils with behavioural difficulties through transitional stages
* enable the development of expertise within the school in dealing with difficult pupils
* enable the development of a social skills programme for primary-aged pupils which could be used in the mainstream classes and in other schools
* provide the opportunity for multidisciplinary work.

The centre, known as the Lynx room, is staffed by a full-time teacher who works closely with the Special Educational Needs Coordinator and class teachers. The centres works with up to eight full-time equivalent pupils per term, but the actual groups at any one time may be no greater than four or five. They will be pupils at risk of exclusion, or may be isolated or withdrawn or suffering low self-esteem. While attending sessions, children engage in work involving raising self-esteem, enhancing literacy and speaking and listening skills, developing social skills, such as cooperation with others through games and circle time, and discussing feelings and reactions. Work activities are related to the National Curriculum being followed by their peers. There is also counselling available for older children.

At the end of the period pupils 'graduate' with a certificate to show their achievements. Pupils are then carefully reintegrated into their own classes when they are monitored and supported. Children who have 'graduated' have continued access to the Lynx Room for support and advice.

The introduction of assertive discipline into the school has provided a structured behaviour policy, which, coupled with the success of the Lynx Room, has led to a fall in exclusions and the numbers at risk of exclusion. The 'caring' nature of the school and the major improvements have been recognised by OFSTED.[57]

"School is an under-rated centre for access to young people – school could be the focus for work of interagency teams and will be a further effective means of bringing children into school, offering a site where teachers, social workers, health workers and possibly criminal justice workers can discuss cases." [58]

Recommendation: Schools should be encouraged, through appropriate funding and the availability of specialist support and training to engage more fully in early intervention work with children and their families experiencing mental health problems. Such work will be further facilitated by a culture which encourages and supports the philosophy of schools educating the 'whole child'.

Recommendation: Special attention must be given to the position of cultural minorities, for example through mentoring schemes supported by members of the relevant communities.

Characteristics of school interventions

A study of 130 controlled studies of early interventions[60] provides strong support for early intervention work in schools. In a frequently cited study, socially isolated children were successfully coached in order to improve their peer relations.[61] In relation to children with externalising problems, cognitive-behavioural techniques emphasising self-monitoring and self-control were used effectively to reduce aggressive and antisocial behaviour.

In a pioneering study of four forms of school intervention, with nearly 600 children found to be showing either neurotic or conduct-type problems, carried out by Kolvin et al,[62] it was concluded that school-based interventions can offer great potential for helping children, and that most of the children reached through such programmes would not otherwise have obtained help. The study also concluded that training teachers in the use of the more effective techniques would have spin-off benefits for other children in their care, and that the continuous, closely-knit social environment of school may be more able to maintain changes achieved in treatment than may contact with a health professional seen solely for the referral problems and for the duration of that problem.[63]

In addition to this, evidence to the Inquiry highlighted the following components of effective practice in schools:
• early identification and assessment
• work with the family as well as the child
• interagency collaboration, particularly with health
• flexible approach, including consultation as well as a direct service from the educational psychology service
• training for staff in schools on mental health issues.

Most effective early intervention programmes take place where there is clear leadership, teachers who are trained and supported, effective links with parents and with other organisations able to offer more specialist services. It is important that schools have a 'whole school' strategy to promote all children's mental health and to create mental health awareness (for further discussion of these issues see Chapter Two).

Recommendation: The recommendations of the Subgroup on Emotional and Behavioural Difficulties to the National Advisory Group on Special Educational Needs should be expanded to include children and young people experiencing mental health problems.

In particular, it is important that all schools must be given guidance and training on developing whole school practice in relation to children with emotional and behavioural difficulties, and this should be extended to promoting children's mental health. This must be backed up with suitable professional development opportunities for teachers in mainstream settings.

We support the development of a simplified special educational needs code of practice, within which we would want to ensure that the needs of children with mental health problems are met through
• effective early assessments
• appropriate school-based interventions
• effective support from external agencies, in particular child and adolescent mental health services and other support services within education services, health authorities and social services.

Recommendation: There should be nationally-funded research on school-based initiatives, long-term funding for those which work, and a programme for the dissemination of good practice.

THE ROLE OF SOCIAL SERVICES, PRIMARY HEALTH CARE AND THE VOLUNTARY SECTOR IN EARLY INTERVENTIONS

Most of the parents giving evidence to the Inquiry sought help from teachers, general practitioners or health visitors initially, although many were disappointed in their quest (see Chapter Four for more detail). It is vitally important that these initial access points are able to respond appropriately to parents without blame or being stigmatising. As we have discussed, it is important that such services are accessible, locally provided and work in partnership with parents, in order that those who require access to preventive or to more specialist help can do so without fear of being blamed. Social service departments play a vital role in providing a range of children's services. Of particular importance in relation to those families at increased risk of developing mental health problems are family centres, especially those which have moved away from a culture of being targeted at parents as a result of child protection concerns and towards a more enabling community orientated role.

Family centres

Family centres which operate an open door policy are better equipped to play a preventive role using toy libraries, mother and toddler clubs, coffee mornings and other drop-in facilities to attract vulnerable families. Families who use these open access facilities, commonly run in partnership with voluntary organisations, can thus access the more specialist help centres can offer, without fear of being stigmatised.[64]

It is important that centres develop a partnership with parents and provide a service which is sensitive to the cultural diversity of local communities. The Audit Commission[65] suggested that family centres could become joint ventures between health, social services, education and voluntary agencies.

THE PRIORY PROJECT, BARNSLEY

The Priory Family Centre is a partnership project between Barnardos, Barnsley Metropolitan Borough Council, City Challenge and Priory Campus Ltd. A multidisciplinary team including nursery workers, social and youth and community workers, volunteers and an administrator provide a range of early care and education and other family support services to families living in the north east corridor of Barnsley. The centre provides day care and early education to students' children and to children referred because of learning and other developmental difficulties by health visitors and social services. Parents study at the college for qualifications which may help them find a way into work, while their children are cared for in a stimulating setting, enjoying the company of other children their age. Local families can make use of a wide range of provision, encompassing holiday respite schemes, after-school clubs and community development activities. As part of a more holistic approach to service provision, social work support is also offered, both in the general sense, including assessments, and more specially to help children and young people who have been sexually abused.[66]

> *"For most people the general practitioner is the one and only port of call. Their awareness and expertise are crucial. I imagine many parents are sent away with false reassurances."*

However, whilst such centres are effective in working with vulnerable families, social service departments have limited funding to develop universal access preventive services. A number of such ventures, in partnership with other statutory and voluntary agencies, existed and/or were planned, but were closed down or halted in the 1980s and 1990s at a time when authorities were forced to make economies. This concern about funding caused social service departments to concentrate resources on its protecting and safeguarding role, vis à vis the most vulnerable children and a fairly narrow interpretation of children in need.

The refocusing initiative, as described in Chapter Two, was warmly welcomed by social service authorities, but there was concern about the extent to which they would be able to divert resources from child protection to family support for children in need, let alone universal preventive services, without prejudicing their protective remit, in the absence of new monies. Thus, the additional monies announced with the comprehensive spending review, *Quality Protects*, etc, needs to be seen against a background of sustained budget cuts, and the recent changes to the method for calculating the Standard Spending Assessment for children's services.

With funding being increasingly tied to specific targets and measures, statutory services are increasingly in the position that the voluntary sector rightly complains of – that of inadequate core funding to give agencies room for creativity. Although, therefore, current government initiatives are welcomed, there is a problem of energies and resources being diverted away from a direct service to the public, to the transaction costs of regularly forming new alliances and working up new bids.

Recommendation: The role of social service departments, with other local authority departments and agencies, eg health, police, probation and the voluntary sector, should be strengthened using Children's Services Plans to create a network of accessible and effective preventive and early intervention services.

Recommendation: There should be further development and evaluation of models of preventive practice by mainstream social work provision, in relation to families whose children are at risk of developing mental health problems.

Role of primary health care in early interventions for children

> *"General practitioners need to be much better trained to recognise mental illness. Swift responses are essential and I feel my son's prognosis was worsened by feeble responses to his condition."*

Primary health professionals could play an increasingly important role in the assessment and early intervention of children with mental health problems.

"General practitioners, health visitors and paediatricians have unique opportunities to engage with parents in the early identification and management of problems, but there has been uneven development of the mental health aspects of their work." [67]

We received evidence of extremely effective practice in relation to general practitioners, health visitors and paediatricians engaged in innovative work in relation to mental health, but we also heard evidence of general practitioners who appeared to be uninformed about mental health issues.

General practitioners and the primary health care team

Scott, in his evidence to the Health Select Committee, stated that 30% of general practitioner consultations with children were related to emotional and behavioural difficulties and it was, therefore, an area of concern for the Inquiry that many general practitioners had little knowledge of child mental health problems.

"General practitioners in particular came in for a lot of criticism regarding their ability to recognise and constructively deal with childhood mental illness. Many parents described being told that there was nothing seriously wrong with their child, or that their children would grow out of their difficult behaviour. For the parents this created a dead end, as it is the general practitioner who most commonly can provide access to more specialist forms of care." [68]

This view of a lack of training and knowledge by general practitioners was substantiated by evidence from professionals and discussions held by Inquiry. Many general practitioners are aware of and frustrated by the limitations of their expertise and lack of time in adequately attending to the mental health needs of children and families.

"Many would like better education and training on the recognition of child mental health problems and advice as to how to more effectively respond to children and families." [69]

General practitioners have a vital role to play, not only in assessing and treating minor problems, but also in signposting parents and their children towards other help and advice, information, self-help groups and, where appropriate, specialist services. These services in turn have an important role to play in both offering general practitioners further training and help with individual children. As the *Young Mind's* report said in relation to general practitioners in Greater Manchester, "general practitioners would value more information about the range of services that could help in their locality. They would also appreciate greater liaison with education and psychology services".

Practices could provide a source of information about advice regarding other local services relating to mental health for parents. A key concern of parents submitting evidence to Inquiry was the lack of information and advice available to them.

"I'd like to see some support for parents – it's very distressing and isolating to have a child with a mental illness."

"The best service offered by our local mental health team is the monthly carers group. I feel it is a lifeline to swap notes with others in similar situations." [71]

"More information on various illnesses should be easily accessible after a diagnosis. You are left to find out information on your own." [70]

Recommendation: General practitioners should become more proactive in the assessment and early intervention of children experiencing mental health problems. This would require

- training for every general practitioner in 'everyday child mental health' difficulties
- the development of active partnerships between general practitioners and specialist mental health services
- the further development and evaluation of models of effective practice in this area
- long-term funding and support of community-based services working in partnership with general practitioner practices.

We received evidence of many innovative schemes that involve general practitioners. In many cases it is the wider primary care team which provides the intervention, but the access is via the general practitioner, and the service is much less stigmatising because it is situated in primary care.

CHILD AND FAMILY COUNSELLOR IN GENERAL PRACTITIONER PRACTICE

This scheme in Dorset has a Child and Family Counsellor who is based within the practice, and also spends time in local schools and homes. As Dr Hayden explained, "Interventions take place at a number of levels, for example with the child and family, or the child and school. The Child and Family Counsellor may work with a child who has behavioural problems and his or her family, while also working with teachers to help them recognise change and respond positively to the child".[72]

The focus of the work is the importance of early intervention, with the counsellor himself being able to offer initial help through a variety of therapeutic approaches, and continue with support if the child and family have been referred on to more specialist services. The counsellor is supervised through the local child and adolescent mental health team. An evaluation of the service found that it was well received by young people and their parents as well as teachers. Aggression amongst children appeared to diminish and academic results improved. A growing number of referrals suggests a high level of acceptability.

"Because of the counsellor's informal approach, he is not seen as a 'mental health professional' and little stigma is attached to contacting him. At the same time interventions are not time consuming." [73]

Primary child mental health care clinics

The training and status of such tier one mental health workers (see Appendices Six and Seven for a description of the 'tiered' structure) raises important questions. Such work is highly skilled, and yet currently there is no recognised skills set or training route for this role. It is important that, within the development of a national strategy for the cross-professional training on children's mental health, attention is given to this area. Such roles could be developed as part of child and adolescent mental health services or within primary care. They play a vital role in linking the specialist services and primary care.

The example of Dorset highlights the important role that general practitioners can increasingly play in the provision of primary care services in relation to mental health. With the development of primary care groups as commissioners of services there is potential for children to be given real priority and for innovative, accessible services to be provided at primary care level.

Recommendation: The role of primary mental health workers needs developing nationally. Such a role can function equally effectively within a single general practitioner practice or group of practices, providing that adequate funding, an effective support network and effective links with other agencies are available.

Role of health visitors

Health visitors have a key role to play in the assessment of and early intervention with children with mental health problems. However, for this to be effective, they need time, training and support. The Government has made proposals for the development of the health visitor role with respect to families, and there will be increasing debate about the focus of their work.

Health visitors seemed, to the parents submitting evidence to us, not to be equipped to recognise and appropriately treat mental health problems, though they did appear willing to work with the parents in seeking further help.

"I first asked for help from my health visitor who tried various behaviour modifying techniques. These didn't work, so when crisis point was reached she got my son referred to the community consultant paediatrician."

Yet, the Inquiry heard a number of positive examples of work with primary health care professionals in the provision of community-based mental health services, particularly the work of Jessie Earle et al in the development of a training pack for health visitors, and that of Hilton Davis et al in his pioneering work setting up a community-based primary care service in South London.[74]

DEVELOPMENT OF A COMMUNITY CHILD AND FAMILY MENTAL HEALTH SERVICE

This service, the Community Child and Family Service, was established with funding from the Lambeth, Southwark and Lewisham Health Authority to develop and evaluate local community child mental health services. It is staffed by three full-time and one part-time child mental health specialists, six part-time parent advisers, each of whom works one day a week, a full-time assistant psychologist and a full-time secretary/administrator.

The specific aims of the service are to
• improve access to and utilisation of child mental health care
• improve the identification and management of the broad range of child and family mental health difficulties in the community
• develop community-based health promotion and prevention programmes.

After carrying out a preliminary needs assessment, which identified the high level of needs within the area, and the broad enthusiasm of primary care professionals for such a service, the Community Child and Family Service has developed a series of specific evaluated projects.

Development of primary health care projects

The Parent Adviser Service

This home-based intervention is carried out by health visitors and community paediatric medical officers specially trained in parenting issues and child behavioural management.

The aims of the intervention are to prevent parents feeling stigmatised or belittled; to empower them to use their own resources effectively to manage difficulties confronting them, and to be with them and support them while they do so. The Parent Adviser's role is to facilitate this process via the development of a respectful relationship with the parents. Initially, families are seen weekly, with the frequency of visits reducing gradually, depending upon the needs identified and the aims negotiated with the parents.

Primary child mental health care clinics

Since Spring 1996, the service has been working with six local general practitioner practices. Within each practice, on-site clinics have been set up for children with emotional and behavioural difficulties and their families, run by child mental health specialists.

Primary prevention of child mental health problems involving health visitors

This project involves trained health visitors conducting promotional interviews before and immediately after all new births, whilst at the same time screening for families at risk of developing child mental health problems. The health visitor then works immediately and intensively with those identified as being in need. It is predicted that the training will enhance health visitors' ability to identify families at risk, improve family function and positively influence the well-being and development of the children.

The development of projects in educational settings

School nurse training programme

The service is also engaged in a number of projects within schools. This project has used the lessons from the Parent Adviser model of work with under fives to run training and supervision for a group of school nurses for school-age children.

Intensive school-based intervention programme

In another project, a clinical psychologist has been working intensively for one day a week in a local primary school. The psychologist has

- carried out direct work with pupils and parents referred by teachers and families themselves
- facilitated small problem-focused groups for pupils on issues such as anger control
- worked with whole classes on health promotion interventions
- provided regular consultation groups for the teaching staff.

Consultation programme for day nursery officers

The service has also provided a regular consultation service for day nursery officers. This involves day nursery staff in the area receiving fortnightly consultation from a member of the service.

Conclusions

This service offers one model for the development of community services, and has been received warmly by those in primary health care, education and social care. The keys to the success of the projects appear to be

- the specialist training of the non-mental health professionals
- the partnership approach between both specialist mental health professionals and community-based and primary care professionals, and between professionals and parents
- the accessibility of the service, both for clients and tier one professionals.

For a fuller description of these projects see Appendix Five.

NATIONAL POLICY AND SERVICE PLANNING IMPLICATIONS

Strategic and policy coordination

The Inquiry welcomes the Government initiatives in related areas, such as *Sure Start, Quality Protects,* the National Priorities Guidance, the National Child Care Strategy, the work of the Social Exclusion Unit, and its current consultation on the family. It is heartening that recent government pronouncements have taken on so much of what practitioners and researchers have recommended.

Recommendation: That all government initiatives on children, the family and education explicitly address mental health issues and that there is a clear cross-departmental government commitment to early intervention for children experiencing mental health problems which should include a commitment to

- develop the capacity of mainstream services, under fives provision, schools and primary care, to recognise and begin to meet the needs of children and their families when difficulties arise
- engage with, not reject, those children and families who are hardest to reach
- early intervention, not just early in the child's life, but early assessment and intervention whenever difficulties arise throughout a child's life
- long-term intervention for those children with more intractable problems
- assess the value of innovative programmes across departmental boundaries, where cost savings may be long-term and to identify long-term funding for successful interventions whether based within local authorities, health authorities, the voluntary sector or those falling between agency responsibilities.

1 Rutter, M (1974) *Dimensions of Parenthood: some myths and suggestions* in Department of Health and Social Security *The Family in Society: dimensions of parenthood* HMSO, London

2 Guralnik, M (ed) (1997) *The Effectiveness of Early Intervention* Brookes, Baltimore

3 Fonagy, P (1998) *Early Influences on Development and Social Inequalities* paper for Sir Donald Acheson's Independent Inquiry into Inequalities in Health

4 Bradley, R H, Whiteside, L, Mundfrom, D J, Casey, P H, Kelleher, K J and Pope, S (1994) *Early indications of resilience and their relation to experiences in the home environments of infants born prematurely and with low birth-weight* Journal of Educational Psychology vol 86 pp346-360

5 Belsky, J and Vondra, J (1989) *Lessons from child abuse: the determinants of parenting* in Cicchetti, D and Carlson, V (eds) *Child Maltreatment. Theory and research on the causes and consequences of child abuse and neglect* Cambridge University Press

6 Easterbrooks, M A Cummings, E M and Emde, R N (1994) *Young children's responses to constructive marital disputes* Journal of Family Psychology vol 8 pp160-169

Jouriles, E N Murphy, C M Farris, A M Smith, D A Richter, J E and Water, E (1991) *Marital adjustment, parental disagreements about childrearing and behaviour problems in boys: increasing the specificity of the marital assessment* Child Development vol 62 pp1424-1433

7 Hetherington, E M Cox, M and Cox, R (1982) *The Effects of Divorce on Parents and Children* Hillsdale, New Jersey

8 Cox, A D Puckering, C Pound, A and Mills, M (1987) *The impact of maternal depression on young children* Journal of Child Psychology and Psychiatry vol 28 pp917-928

9 Sampson, R J and Laub, J H (1993) *Crime in the Making: Pathways and turning points through life* Harvard University Press

Farrington, D P Loeber, R G, van Kammen, W B (1990) *Long-term criminal outcomes of hyperactivity-impulsivity-attention deficit and conduct in childhood* in Robins, L N and Rutter, M (eds) *Straight and Devious Pathways from Childhood to Adulthood* Cambridge University Press

10 Patterson, G R (1982) *Coercive Family Process* Castalia

11 Offord, D and Bennett, K J (1994) *Conduct disorder: long-term outcomes and intervention effectiveness* Journal of the American Academy of Child and Adolescent Psychiatry vol 33 pp1069-1078

12 Cohen, P Cohen, J and Brook, J (1993) *An epidemiological study of disorders in late childhood and adolescence II Persistence of disorders* Journal of Child Psychology and Psychiatry vol 34 pp869-897

Ollendick, T H and King, N J (1994) *Diagnosis, assessment and treatment of internalising problems in children: The role of longitudinal data* Journal of Consulting and Clinical Psychology vol 62 pp918-927

13 Campbell, S B (1995) *Behaviour problems in pre-school children: A review of recent research* Journal of Child Psychology and Psychiatry vol 36 pp113-149

14 White, J Moffitt, T E Earls, F Robins, L and Silva, P (1990) *How early can we tell? Pre-school indicators of boys' conduct disorder and delinquency* Criminology vol 28 pp507-533

15 Johnson, Z Howell, F and Molloy, B (1993) *Community Mothers Programme: randomised controlled trial of non-professional intervention in parenting* BMJ vol 306 pp1449-1452

16 Oakley, A Rajan, L and Grant, A (1990) *Social support and pregnancy outcome* British Journal of Obstetrics and Gynaecology vol 97 pp155-162

17 Murray, L (1992) *The impact of post-natal depression on infant development* Journal of Child Psychology and Psychiatry vol 33 pp543-561

18 Goepfert, M Webster, J and Seeman, M (eds) (1996) *Parental Psychiatric Disorder. Distressed Parents and their families* Cambridge University Press

19 Cooper, P and Murray, L (1997) *Postpartum depression and child development* Psychological Medicine vol 27 pp253-260

20 Cooper, P and Murray, L (1997) as in no 19

21 Professional evidence to the Inquiry

22 Cox, J L Holden, J M and Sagovsky, R (1987) *Detection of post-natal depression: development of the 10-item Edinburgh Post-natal Depression Scale* British Journal of Psychiatry vol 150 pp782-6

23 Hodnett, E D and Roberts, I (1997) *Home-based social support for socially disadvantaged mothers* in Neilson, J P Crowther, C A Hodnett, E D Hofmeyr, G J Keirse, M J N C (eds) *Pregnancy and Childbirth Module of the Cochrane Database of Systematic Reviews* issue no 2 Cochrane Library

24 Hodnett, E D (1997) *Support from caregivers during childbirth* in Neilson et al as in no 23

25 Elliot, S A Sanjack, M Leverton, T F (1988) *Parents' groups in pregnancy: a preventive for post-natal depression?* in Gottlieb, B J (ed) *Marshalling Social Support: Formats, Process and Effects* Sage, London

26 Elliott, S A (1989) *Psychological strategies in the prevention and treatment of post-natal depression* Psychological Aspects of Obstetrics and Gynaecology Ballieres Clinical Obstetrics and Gynaecology vol 3 pp879-903

27 Wiecek, A Kumar, R Hirst, A D et al (1991) *Increased sensitivity of dopamine receptors and recurrence of affective psychosis after childbirth* BMJ vol 303 pp613-616

28 Oates, M (1996) *Post-natal mental illness: its importance and management* in Goepfert, M Webster, J and Seeman, M (eds) (1996) *Parental Psychiatric Disorder. Distressed Parents and their families* Cambridge University Press

29 Goepfert et al (1996) as in no 18

30 Bronfenbrenner, U (1979) *The Ecology of Human Development: Experiments by Nature and Design* Harvard University Press

31 Fonagy, P (1996) Plenary address at the 6th World Congress of the World Association for Infant Mental Health

32 Barker, W Anderson, R and Chambers, C (1994) *Child Protection: the impact of the child development programme* Department of Social Work, Bristol University

33 MacDonald, G Roberts, H (1995) *What Works in the Early Years? Effective interventions for children and their families in health, social welfare, education and child protection Part III* Barnados, Essex

34 Utting, D (1995) *Family and Parenthood: supporting families, preventing breakdown* Joseph Rowntree Foundation, York

35 Miller, G E and Prinz, R J (1990) *Enhancement of social learning family interventions for child conduct disorder* Psychological Bulletin vol 108 pp291-237

36 Yoshikawa, H (1994) *Prevention as cumulative protection: effects of early family support and education on chronic delinquency and its risk* Psychological Bulletin vol 115 pp28-54

37 Centre for the Study of Social Policy (1990) *Helping families grow strong. New directions in social policy* Paper from the USA Colloquium on *Public Policy and Family Support* quoted in Pugh et al (1994)

38 Shepherd, J P and Farrington, D P (1995) *Preventing crime and violence: pre-school education, early family support and situational prevention can be effective* BMJ vol 310 pp271-272

39 McGuire, J and Earls, J (1991) *Prevention of psychiatric disorders in early childhood* Journal of Child Psychology and Psychiatry vol 32 pp129-153

40 Horacek, H J Ramey, C T Campbell, F A Hoffman, K P Fletcher, R H (1987) *Predicting school failure and assessing early intervention with high risk children* Journal of the American Academy of Child and Adolescent Psychiatry vol 26 pp758-763

41 Barth, R P (1991) *An experimental evaluation of in-home child abuse prevention services* Child Abuse and Neglect vol 15 pp363-375

42 Fonagy, P (1998) as in no 3

43 Cicchetti, D and Toth, S L (1995) *A developmental psychopathology perspective on child abuse and neglect* Journal of the American Academy of Child and Adolescent Psychiatry vol 34 pp541-565

44 Oliver, C Smith, M and Barker, S (1998) *Effectiveness of Early Interventions* in HM Treasury Cross Departmental Review of Provision for Young Children Supporting Papers

45 Professional evidence to the Inquiry from Barnardos

46 Oliver, C Smith, M and Barker, S (1998) as in no 44

47 Parent at Search Conference

48 Parent's evidence to the inquiry

49 Department for Education Circular (94)9

50 Kurtz, Z (1996) *Treating Children Well* Mental Health Foundation, London

51 NHS Health Advisory Service (1995) *Together We Stand. The Commissioning Role and Management of Child and Adolescent Mental Health Services* HMSO, London

52 Audit Commission (1996) *Misspent Youth Young People and Crime* HMSO, London

53 Evidence to Inquiry from J Thewlis, Institute of Education

54 Hayden, C (1997) *Children excluded from primary school: debates, evidence, responses* Open University Press, Buckingham

55 Durlak, J A (1995) *School-based Prevention Programs for Children and Adolescents* Sage, Thousand Oaks

56 Kurtz, Z (1996) as in no 50

57 as in no 53

58 Evidence to the Inquiry from Dr Carl Parsons, Canterbury Christchurch College

59 Webster-Stratton, C and Hancock, L (1998) *Training for parents of young children with conduct problems: Content, methods and therapeutic processes* in Schaefer, C E and Briesmeister, J M (eds) *Handbook of Parent Training* pp98-152 John Wiley and Sons

60 Durlak, J A (1995) as in no 55

61 Durlak, J A (1995) as in no 55

62 Kolvin, I Garside, R F Nicol, A R MacMillan, A Wolstenholme, F and Leitch I M (1981) *Help Starts Here: The maladjusted child in the ordinary school* Tavistock Publications, London

63 Roth, A and Fonagy, P (1996) *What Works for Whom: A critical review of psychotherapy research* Guildford Press, NY

64 Gibbons, J Thorpe, S and Wilkinson, P (1990) *Family Support and Prevention: studies in local areas* HMSO, London

65 Audit Commission (1994) *Seen But Not Heard – Coordinating Community Child Health and Social Services for Children in Need* HMSO, London

66 Lloyd, E et al (1997) *Today and Tomorrow: Investing in our Children* Barnados, Essex

67 Kurtz, Z (1996) as in no 50

68 O'Connell, P (1999) *Parents' evidence to the Inquiry* Mental Health Foundation, London (in press)

69 Professional evidence to Inquiry

70 Parent's evidence to the Inquiry

71 Parent's evidence to the Inquiry

72 Hayden, A (1997) *A GP-based child and adolescent mental health service* Young Minds Magazine 30 p13

73 Evidence to the Inquiry from Dr Anne Hayden, GP, Dorset

74 Day, C and Davis, H (1999) *Community child mental health services: A framework for the development of parenting initiatives* submitted to the Journal of Clinical Child Psychology and Psychiatry

Davis, H Spurr, P Cox, et al (1997) *A description and evaluation of a community child mental health service* Clinical Child Psychology and Psychiatry vol 2 pp221-238

Day, C Davis, H Hind, R (1998) *The development of a community child and family mental health service* Child: Care, Health and Development vol 24 pp487-500

Services for children and young people experiencing mental health problems

" We cannot speak too highly of the dedicated team of social workers in our area, who support, advise and befriend our son."

INTRODUCTION

" You are expected to get on with it, without any real or meaningful support. No support to assist you over the shock of diagnosis."

So far this report has been concerned with the promotion of all children's mental health, and early interventions for children of all ages largely within mainstream services. The ability of these services to deliver effective support and interventions to children and their parents is predicated on there being the expertise and support within those mainstream agencies to deliver this work, and also on the availability and existence of specialist support and input from mental health professionals as and when necessary. With increasing emphasis being placed on the development of early intervention programmes, the challenge will be to ensure that there are the range and numbers of such professionals available to support this early work.

In addition, there will always be those children who require specialist mental health input, whether in the form of support and treatment within the community, or within in-patient settings. It is in relation to the needs of these children that we received the most evidence, particularly from parents and young people, but also from practitioners and researchers working in the field.

The messages from this evidence were uncompromising, and consistently stressed the necessity of greatly increased attention and priority for mental health. Children's mental health services are at last on the policy agenda for the Government, and there is increasing awareness of the importance of addressing the many complex issues around the development of services for children and young people experiencing mental health problems. However, the task which confronts all of those seeking to develop appropriate, sensitive and accessible services for children and young people remains an enormous challenge. Many of those areas which currently have the worst records in the development of child and adolescent mental health services will be the least ready to access the limited resources currently being offered by government to do so.

There are also real challenges in developing services which are accessible, especially for those who are the most vulnerable; of creating a culture which embraces partnership and consultation at all levels and which is truly committed to providing appropriate services for all of our communities.

This chapter will aim to examine issues relating to child and adolescent mental health services based on the range of evidence received from the Inquiry, from professionals working within health, social services and voluntary agencies, and parents and children who have experience of using those services.

It was clear from the evidence that despite the increased priority for child and adolescent mental health services over the last few years, they are still "essentially unplanned and historically determined. Their distribution is patchy and they are variable in quality and composition".[1]

RESOURCES AND PLANNING

The most common concern in the professional evidence was the lack of resources for child and adolescent mental health services allied with the increase in demand for services and the increasing severity of problems being seen.

"Lack of resources, a massive increase in demand, and an apparent increase in the seriousness of the type of referrals made. The effect of this increase in demand has been that we have moved away from a waiting list of two to three weeks up to six or seven months for low priority cases. It also means that we are not able to meet perfectly reasonable demands from the local authority for consultation services to special schools, children's homes and so on." [2]

"There is a major under investment in children's mental health services and this has to be addressed at a national as well as a local level." [3]

The majority of child and adolescent mental health services giving evidence were clear that the adequate funding of child and adolescent mental health services has to be tackled from a multifaceted perspective, taking on board the needs of primary care providers, tier three services and, in addition to this, the need for adequate specialist tier four services.

"There has been a failure in recent years by central government to appreciate there should be investment both at primary care level and the specialist level, to meet overall child and adolescent mental health needs. This has resulted in the absence of services at primary care level, and the development of large numbers of private providers at specialist level, which are swallowing resources that could otherwise be spent on the development of an integrated, state-funded service." [4]

Those giving evidence understood that an increase in resources alone could not bring about the necessary changes, but believed that lasting improvements could not be made without increased financial commitment. The different funding mechanisms of the statutory agencies and the interdependence of agencies meant that reduction in capacity by one agency resulted in extra costs falling on others.

Action at government level

We welcome the new National Priorities Guidance for Health and Social Care, issued in September 1998, with its commitment to "improve provision of appropriate, high quality care and treatment for children and young people by building up locally-based child and adolescent mental health services. This should be achieved through improved staffing levels and training provision at all tiers; improved liaison between primary care, specialist child and adolescent mental health services, social services and other agencies". The £84 million, which has been set aside to achieve this over the next three years, is a welcome first step towards the necessary increase in resources.

Yet, despite the wealth of guidance and increasing commitment to the importance of children's mental health, child and adolescent mental health services remain "essentially unplanned and historically determined", "fragile and vulnerable to the financial and political tensions that exist between statutory authorities".[5]

While it is not possible to overstate the need for extra resource, attention must also be paid to the delivery of services which is affected by the availability of sufficient trained professionals, their ability to work effectively together despite their differing professional perspectives, and the willingness of different agencies to cooperate in service planning and delivery.

Recommendation: The Government urgently needs to address the inadequacies of the current services. Legislation should establish a statutory duty for local authorities, health authorities, social services authorities and education authorities to cooperate in promoting children's mental health. The legislation should require government to develop a National Service Framework (similar to that developed for adult mental health services) for children's mental health, with clear targets for health, social services and education authorities – in order that each shall meet their responsibilities to work together and meet the needs of these children and young people. The detail of such a framework will obviously need a great deal of discussion, and we would therefore recommend the setting up of a steering group led by government in order to achieve this.

Recommendation: A Standing Commission (Advisory Committee) on the Emotional and Mental Health of Children should be established to provide the national leadership to oversee the production and implementation of the national framework and to develop a framework for cross-professional training.

Such a coordinating body would obviously need to have regard to other planning and commissioning groups working in the area, particularly Children's Services Plans, the work of the youth offending teams, Early Years Development Plans, primary care commissioning groups, etc. There is already a great deal of activity in the area of children's services, but we believe that without a clear focus on children's mental health at both a local and a national level, which is linked into ministerial decision-making, the opportunity to develop effective services and practice nationally will be lost.

The components of a comprehensive service

"Child and adolescent services need to be implemented within a tiered structure with resources matched to different levels of need."

The adoption of the following overall targets for a child and adolescent mental health service has been suggested.[6]

For Communities up to 250,000, each area should have
- a primary care team, with specialist support and input from outreach child and adolescent mental health services
- adequately staffed solo professional and multidisciplinary services providing day and out-patient services – these should work closely with coterminous local authority social services and education teams
- solo professionals to have ready access to multidisciplinary services, if staff are not also members of such services – it is important that staff are not isolated
- intensive day treatment provision to be available for families of under fives for parenting problems and for school-age children
- specialist services to provide concentrated input into areas of high need, such as special schools, local authority family centres, residential homes and paediatric clinics.

For communities up to 750,000, in-patient facilities for children and adolescents are to be provided. The Royal College of Psychiatrists has estimated that, for a total population of 250,000, in-patient provision should be two to four beds for children and four to six beds for adolescents up to 16.

For communities up to 3,000,000, there are rare and difficult to manage conditions for which highly specialised services are required. These can be divided into
- those conditions requiring complex assessment, such as pervasive development disorders, post-traumatic stress disorders
- difficult to treat conditions, such as severe conduct disorder, including those needing secure accommodation, neuropsychiatric disorders, and post-traumatic stress disorder, for example.

It has been suggested that a five-star 'comprehensive service' for a health district would include[7]
- a multidisciplinary out-patient team with 10 clinical staff
- two multidisciplinary day-patient services (shared with another district) with six clinical staff each, one for adolescents, one for children
- one to three beds available on regional in-patient units.

Within this model, there would be an open referrals system and a wide range of out-patient and day-patient assessment for children and adolescents up to the age of 18, and young adults with children. Assessments would also be carried out in schools and social care settings. A wide range of therapeutic approaches would be available for out-patients and day-patients. Extensive consultation with other professionals would be offered with the emphasis on prevention and early detection of psychiatric disorder. Teaching, would be provided to a variety of professionals in different settings. There should also be scope for research and audit.

There was a clear consensus throughout the evidence and discussions that the tiered structure of services, as laid out in a number of key documents, principally *Together We Stand*, was the most effective way of delivering child and adolescent mental health services. However, although many areas have made great strides in putting services in place, comprehensive services are still lacking in many parts of the country.

Piecemeal development of services

"Luck seems to play far too great a part in receiving good service - living in the right place at the right time, having a knowledgeable and helpful general practitioner, having able social workers, having local services that cooperate with one another - all these seem to depend on luck." [8]

The evidence indicated a strong commitment to implementing the recommendations within the HAS report and other government guidance. However, in practice, there remains an enormous disparity around the country in the level of child and adolescent mental health services available.

In many areas, child and adolescent mental health services were widely dispersed, sometimes appearing to operate in competition with each other. Often services were dependent on a few key personnel and overall uncertain ownership. In other areas, child and adolescent mental health services were comparatively well funded, with clear clinical and managerial input, and explicit academic support. These models of innovative and effective practice were, however, in the minority of examples of child and adolescent mental health services.

> "We've gone through 10 years of a very difficult time. We were coping with no help. It took five months to get a psychiatrist even with an urgent case." [9]

Lack of specialist resources

A clear theme to emerge from both the professional, parents and young people's evidence was a frustration at the lack of specialist services for children and young people experiencing more severe mental health problems. The majority of parents who submitted evidence to the Inquiry wrote movingly about their struggles to find the appropriate help for their troubled children. They often had to wait years between first becoming concerned for their child and receiving appropriate help.

For many, when specialist help finally was made available, it was often miles away from home, resulting in having to travel long distances in order to visit and maintain contact with their children.

> "We eventually got her into..... in London. They expect a lot of input from the parents, which is a good thing. But living in Cardiff - it is really stressful for us all making the trips once a week to visit."

Parents and professionals were united in their concerns about the lack of specialist services on the ground. The Inquiry heard the example of Norfolk Health Trust, whose nearest in-patient facility for children was in Cambridge, 65 miles from Norwich and 85 miles from Yarmouth.

> *"The key issue affecting our service is lack of resources. We have suffered a massive increase in demand, and an apparent increase in the seriousness of the type of referrals made. The increase in referrals has been about 9-10%, compound, over the last 15 years. The expansion of staff has been minimal, and the proportion of money spent on mental health across the age band has diminished."*

This evidence endorses that submitted to the Health Select Committee. For example, the Royal College of Nursing and Royal College of Psychiatrists, in evidence to the Health Select Committee, drew attention to the 1994 survey of 60 units indicating a reduction in the number of beds available in those units of almost 20% over the previous three years, with at least seven units having lost all their beds, and others being threatened with closure.

In relation to the planning of specialist care there is "no evidence that in general, the level or type of service is based on strategic planning to meet defined needs of the local child population". Also that there is "no relationship.... between the provision of specialists and the indicators of likely need". [10]

DEVELOPING AND COMMISSIONING SERVICES

The commissioning of services should be based on local needs assessment and what is known about effective practice and proven interventions.

In many areas, despite real improvements, the picture still appears to be one of
- poor dialogue between health, education and social services commissioners
- absence of a comprehensive strategy for child and adolescent mental health services
- a lack of assessment of the mental health needs of children and adolescents
- lack of effective collaboration between commissioners, especially in health, regarding very specialist supradistrict services
- poor understanding and inadequate knowledge in relation to child and adolescent mental health services issues

- lack of relevant data on child and adolescent mental health services for planning and monitoring.

Development of primary care groups may well mean increased input from those nearer to service delivery, but it is not clear as yet what the impact of this will be.

Recommendation: The commissioning of child and adolescent mental health services should remain with health authorities for the foreseeable future. Primary care groups need to develop the expertise to consider services in a holistic way.

Joint commissioning

Research into the development of child and adolescent mental health services in the North West[11] revealed that "it is most pleasing to report that, as recommended by government guidance, there was a universal awareness of the requirements to plan on a multiagency basis and to provide on a multidisciplinary basis. There was an appreciation of the desirability of child and adolescent mental health services to be linked both to the mental health services and the wider children's services, including the child protection services and education services".

However, as with the evidence submitted to the Inquiry, this research found wide differences in the planning and development by the 15 North West Authorities.

Structural issues having an impact on service commissioning and delivery include
- the current inability of health and social services to delegate to each other (this is now changing)
- the differences in political clout, dynamics and accountability between social services and health authorities and social service departments and primary care commissioning groups
- the differences in the budget and funding systems of social service departments and health authorities.

Whilst there is no consensus on the desirability of joint commissioning of child and adolescent mental health services, the need for joint planning and interagency working is acknowledged as vital.

Recommendation: Models of good practice in coordination between a variety of agencies should be developed, evaluated and effectively disseminated to the practitioners on the ground.

Input from parents and children to service development

Evidence to the Inquiry shows that the involvement of informal groups, networks of carers, parents' self-help groups and of young people in decision-making processes relating to child and adolescent mental health services is minimal. Parents were clear that professionals should consult them in relation to the provision of services.

" I think parents and, in certain cases, older children who are now well enough to speak up for themselves about their experiences, good and bad, should be included on health committees, education committees and government bodies." [13]

> "Consultation is about taking advice from young people, asking their opinions, and not just about recording their experiences... Consultation is a practical matter, and is about human rights and ethical practice, not about elegant academic research. Agencies need to meet young people half-way, and equally those who work with young people in the community need to recognise the need to communicate effectively with the health service." [14]

"I think parents, young people and children's views should be heard. They are the ones that have to live with disorders and they are the ones who have a better understanding than professionals." [12]

"Break down the barriers between the health service, schools, social services and police. In situations like ours, where there is no single, obvious problem, each of the above groups thinks it is someone else's problem." [17]

Such consultation must include a responsiveness and sensitivity to all those using the services, including those from black and minority ethnic communities. We believe strongly that effective child and adolescent mental health services are those based within the community – meaning in practice that such services should be accountable to those communities they are purporting to serve, and appropriate mechanisms set up to facilitate this.

Effective interventions

One of the clear messages to emerge from the professional evidence was the importance of further research and evaluation into 'what works'. The absence of a substantial body of information or strong evidence of the effectiveness of psychological and pharmacological treatments for children and young people is well recognised and moves to remedy this, through the establishment of organisations such as Focus within the Royal College of Psychiatry, are to be encouraged. Yet, while we know that there is a great deal of work that needs to be done in this area, the evaluation that does exist on the effectiveness of treatments that services offer provides strong grounds for optimism.

The *National Child and Adolescent Mental Health Epidemiological Needs Assessment* summarises, in a fairly cautious and critical manner, what is known about treatments.[15] In addition to this, there is increasing evidence for the efficacy of a range of treatments, ranging from medications such as Methylphenidate for hyperactivity disorders to a range of psychotherapies. See Appendix Four for a summary of findings relating to a number of mental health problems encountered in children and young people.

At present, there are few examples of child and adolescent mental health treatment that can unequivocally demonstrate their effectiveness. However, substantial progress has been made in identifying the range of interventions that have the potential to benefit children with mental health problems and their families. However, even these proven interventions are not available to all those who need them and research results are not widely disseminated. Alongside a greater commitment to and funding of research in this area, it is important that there is a commitment to their being the necessary resources and skills to translate this into effective practice at a service delivery level.

"The root of the difficulty in applying research findings to improve services is that the services are mostly not conceived of as a system of care. Thus. if mental health is the desired outcome, we can only hope to achieve it if services are planned and enabled to work together as a system with this as a common aim." [16]

Recommendation: The Department of Health Research and Development programme and the Medical Research Council should give greater priority to research and the evaluation of interventions and to the effective dissemination of research to practitioners in all relevant fields.

INTERAGENCY WORKING

It is clear from the evidence to us that effective multiagency working within child and adolescent mental health services, and between child and adolescent mental health services and other services, is key to effective service delivery.

"At present, multidisciplinary teams are under-funded, over-subscribed and breaking up due to changes in local government. The admissions units are also under-funded and many are being closed. This means that some children known to be at high risk and with a poor prognosis, eg children excluded from schools, children 'in care' and children with learning difficulties, may not receive appropriate help because of difficulties in cross-agency collaboration and lack of basic service provision." [18]

Multiagency working was the second most cited key issue (after funding) in the evidence from those agencies working at tiers three and four. When working well it was described as being highly effective, but there were frequent problems. The most common were
- lack of available staffing
- the fragmentation of services both within and between agencies
- lack of priority accorded to children's mental health services in health, social services and education.

THE WIRRAL MODEL

Wirral Child and Adolescent Mental Health Services is providing a new multidisciplinary service which works in a 'core and cluster' model with a main team and outreach teams based in general practitioners' surgeries.

Wirral Child and Adolescent Mental Health Services was described as being a well-funded service, receiving about 10% more funding that other child and adolescent mental health services. However, it was argued that they saw more clients and therefore maintained good value for money.

The breakdown of spending for the service was described as follows:
- 20% on psychiatrist
- 25% on psychologist, child psychotherapists
- 10% on manager and secretaries
- 10% on non-staff costs, eg training and telephones.

As part of the service, there is a team for children with learning disabilities, and a team for children aged 16-19. Other parts of the service include a day provision with education in collaboration with teachers and a small psychotherapy team. The service offers a range of different interventions, eg a risk team, parenting groups, complex cases group and family therapy. The team was described as working effectively with other agencies, such as social services, education and paediatrics. Regular meetings are held with senior personnel within education and social services, although no funding was received from social services.

Strong links with other agencies, such as general practitioners in various localities and education, meant that the team had a high referral rate. However, there is a commitment to see patients within eight weeks, with more urgent cases seen within two weeks.

"Sometimes it seems like there are either too many professionals from different areas involved or there is no help and support available. Getting the balance right would be ideal." [20]

Roles and responsibilities

Evidence showed the need for the development of effective working models for collaboration between agencies which had very real differences of approach and different lines of accountability.

> "It is inevitable that mental health is the concern of a wide range of people and agencies, logically the health service should be seen as responsible, but there is ambiguity as to what constitutes the sort of mental health problem which can best be dealt with by health. It is neither logical or practical to expect the health service to respond to all such problems affecting socialisation or education. Interagency liaison at all levels becomes inevitable. Management of this is a key issue." [19]

The differences in approach across disciplines within child and adolescent mental health services was seen by many of those submitting evidence as being a hindrance to joint working. The importance of developing multiagency assessments of children and young people was stressed as being fundamental in overcoming this. This assessment could be carried out by a multiagency screening process, reviews being carried out for the most complex cases by multidisciplinary teams and with all disciplines being fully represented on planning, managerial and strategy groups.

The existence of parallel services, with little or no relationship with each other, was experienced as being particularly negative and frustrating by the parents who submitted evidence. For nearly all the parents who submitted evidence, the experiences of seeking help for their children appeared to follow a similar pattern: that of a seemingly endless round of appointments with different professionals and agencies ranging from psychologists, psychiatrists and paediatricians, through to counsellors, social services and even, in desperation, local MPs. Many of the parents experienced a bewildering range of professionals, the majority of whom did not appear to have had appropriate support to offer the parents or their children.

Many parents felt that the lack of communication between the different agencies, their different approaches and, often, different diagnosis regarding their children's problems had reduced their own abilities to cope.

"We experienced real difficulties in communication between all the different agencies. We've seen so many specialists all saying different things. We're really angry at the immense waste of time and energy this has caused – especially when you have so little to share." [21]

Linked to this was the parent's direct experience of the conflict between the different professional agendas, which again they felt impacted on the care and support their children and themselves received.

"My son was diagnosed as having attention deficit hyperactivity disorder which was a huge relief. It had taken us ages to finally get a diagnosis. Then the social worker came, and said that it wasn't attention deficit hyperactivity disorder, it was behavioural problems caused by us. It makes you so angry – you just don't know who to believe. All that we want is to be able to get some help for our boy, but everybody's telling us different things. Eventually, we went privately to get a diagnosis. Well, you have to don't you?"

In Tower Hamlets, there are three multidisciplinary teams which are generally viewed as functioning well and offering a quality service, keeping waiting lists to a minimum despite massive increase in referrals over the last 10 years. Areas which are seen to be working particularly well are

- a generally non-critical, non-stigmatising approach to families, wherein areas of strength are recognised and acknowledged, as well as the difficulties currently being experienced
- good relationships within the multidisciplinary teams, such that the separate skills and knowledge of each professional group are recognised and respected
- relationships of mutual respect with other professional groups operating within the Borough, both in the statutory and voluntary sectors, such that referrals are made appropriately where problems present demanding a combined approach, resources can be combined effectively, eg in the establishment of a multiagency service for young people who sexually abuse.

Unless there is high level agreement on agency responsibilities and an integrated, coordinated response, parents and young people will continue to feel that no one is prepared to take responsibility for providing help.

Recommendation: Health authorities should have lead statutory responsibility for the provision of child and adolescent mental health services. Social service departments and education authorities should have specific, defined responsibilities. This would be a clear component of the proposed National Service Framework.

Philosophy and language

There are different philosophies and models of diagnosis, treatment and care operating in child mental health. There are distinct views on what constitutes mental health, the most effective interventions, the desirable balance between prevention and treatment. This leads to different conceptualisations between different agencies and professions. This can be exacerbated by differences in law and resourcing. Social service departments refer to children in need defined by the Children Act. Within the education system, there are processes and resources to assist children with emotional and behavioural disorders. The police and courts have other ways of accessing resources for children in trouble and the health professions have a range of treatments for children with defined mental health disorders. Many of these children have similar characteristics, but the lack of shared definitions means that it is often arbitrary which service they receive.

The issue of language, the tendency still to use different conceptual frameworks, can create barriers to joint working. We believe that language problems can be overcome, especially by mapping and building on the broad levels of agreement that can be found. This will, however, require a real commitment on the part of all those involved, in addition to an injection of much needed resources in relation to bricks and mortar, service running costs, increased staffing and training to facilitate this.

Recommendation: Ring-fenced resources should be available for jointly commissioned children's services with a mental health remit, from education, health and social service departments.

Lack of effective relationships between primary care professionals and specialist services

Evidence from general practitioners in particular expressed their frustration in relation to child and adolescent mental health services. Chapter Three showed that the interface between primary care services, schools, general practitioners and family centres needs to be actively managed. We heard of examples of child and adolescent mental health services engaged in innovative schemes to improve links with primary care.

" When any support, help, etc are working in different areas or on different assumptions, the child is confused and becomes difficult to deal with." [22]

> "The Government needs to take children's mental health issues far more seriously and provide for this."

> *"We are interpreting the health advisory service 'tier two' concept by establishing multiagency community-based clinics which are the natural first point of call for staff in primary services, whether that be the general practitioner primary team, schools, social services, field teams, etc. These are proving to be very popular with service planners and we see this as an important provision for locality-based services."* [23]

However, such examples of creative working are not being consistently developed around the country. Even though all those submitting evidence stressed the importance of effective primary care provision, it appears that "really effective working with primary health care is sporadic throughout the country. That developed within our own service is probably amongst the most clearly articulated and evaluated, but still heavily limited geographically. It needs to be constantly reaffirmed that the vast majority of child mental health problems are encountered by primary health care and teachers, rather than specialist services. Overall, there is no strong commitment to prevention".[24]

Staffing issues in multidisciplinary working

The effectiveness of interagency working and multidisciplinary teams will depend in part on the relationship between individuals from different professions. We have seen that there are real differences in conceptual framework and approaches between professions. Issues of status, salary and training can all stand in the way of multidisciplinary working. These difficulties can all be overcome by good management, clarity about accountability and shared training, but this needs the commitment of all the agencies.

Several parents advocated using multidisciplinary approaches to assessing the mental health needs of children in the hope that a broad centralised knowledge base would help ensure that children would not 'slip through the net' or become subject to conflicting ideas of treatment.[25]

> "Sometimes it seems like there are either too many professionals from different areas involved or there is no help or support available." [26]

As many of the parents had negative experiences of dealing with professionals with limited knowledge and understanding of their children's problems, it is not surprising that many wanted professionals to have better training in order to recognise and treat childhood mental illness and its effects on the family.

> "Education is vital. Schools have little awareness of mental health issues. This should be incorporated at teacher training stage."

There are important issues to be dealt with in relation to the staffing of multiagency services. The most prominent of these relate to status, salary and training differentials, management hierarchies, priorities, staff's ability to commit exclusively to child and adolescent mental health services or be drawn into other services, the existence or not of clinical autonomy and clinical accountability, and the reluctance by different professional groups to concede power. Urgent attention needs to be given to the lack of suitably qualified staff in all areas, and the need for training for multidiscipline working.

Recommendation: The Department of Health with The Royal College of Psychiatrists, The Royal College of Nursing and The British Psychological Society should commission a comprehensive audit of needs and an analysis of present and future staffing requirements in all services, and develop an appropriate staff development and recruitment strategy.

CORNWALL CHILD AND FAMILY SERVICES

In 1994, Cornwall District Health Authority requested an HAS review of child and adolescent mental health services. The report which HAS commissioners produced identified some areas of good practice, but also identified fragmentation of services and general lack of coordination between providers.

One of the major problems identified was providing a consistent service to children and young people and one which allowed them access to the most appropriate person to meet their needs. Referrals were often made inappropriately, for example a consultant psychiatrist could be referred a child whose problems could have been solved by an education welfare officer. "It was clear that much close interagency involvement was needed… and it seemed clear that it was in the best interests of the children concerned that agencies should share responsibility for dealing with their problems and not either attempt to solve problems independently or, for financial reasons, pass them from one agency to another."

Therefore, a three-tier system of service delivery was devised.

- Tier one acknowledges work already going on in the community – recognising the strengths in school pastoral systems and linking them into the system, along with work done by health visitors and general practitioners.

- Tier two of the service is intended to be particularly supportive of schools which are experiencing difficulties with the management of pupils. The second tier is the most innovative aspect of the arrangement in that it brings together all the staff of the present county council psychological service (school psychological service) with the non-medical staff of the health care trusts. Staff of the psychiatric service have been seconded to the County Psychological Service for a three-year period. They are under the linked management of the Child Education Psychologist and for operational purposes are jointly managed by the Clinical Manager of the Child and Psychiatric Services and a Senior Educational Psychologist.

Teams of staff are based in area centres to enable services to be delivered locally. There are built-in links with the local advisory teachers for children with emotional and behavioural disorders and also links with education welfare officers who can link between schools and the area centres on a regular basis.

- Tier three comprises consultant child psychiatrists and the specialist therapists. This service is delivered in West Cornwall from a centre based at a hospital in Truro and in the East by the Plymouth Health Care Trust staff based in Plymouth. Each agency, social services, health and education, contributes to a joint fund to be used by the management of Child and Family Services to seek alternative in-county solution for children with emotional and behavioural disorders who would otherwise be treated expensively outside the county.

This new joint service, the Cornwall Child and Family Services, is seen as a community service to be accessed by schools, general practitioners, health visitors and social workers and has an open referral system to parents and young people themselves.

Recommendation: The Government should establish a cross-departmental group to develop a strategy for effective cross-professional training on children's mental health, at pre-professional and post-qualifying levels.

LOOKED-AFTER CHILDREN

One of the areas of gravest concern for the Inquiry was the compelling evidence of the lack of support and help for those children who are deemed to be most challenging – those who are 'looked after' by the local authority – whether fostered, in children's homes or in more secure accommodation, and particularly those children/young people who are in young offender institutions/prisons (this group will be discussed in Chapter Five).

> "Children in care constitute a deprived and needy group of youngsters, who are at high risk of developing mental health disorders, which often persist in adult life. Unfortunately, there is little, if any, provision of mental health services that target their needs." [27]

Research submitted to us, concerning the health of young people in care, by Dr Bob Broad, revealed that, of those children taking part in this research
- 17% had long-term mental illnesses or disorders
- 35% had deliberately self-harmed since age of 15 or 16
- 60% had thought about taking their own life – and 40% had tried to do so.

We received much anecdotal evidence from young people who had been in care regarding the lack of mental health services and support.

Current arrangements for providing psychiatric and other specialist services to children in care are grossly inadequate, and we heard that children have to wait as long as two years before being assessed for treatment.

> "The key issue is the lack of availability of psychiatric and psychological assessments preventing intervention commencing at a stage when more positive outcomes can be expected." [28]

Looked-after children can be a challenging group to work with, who require a particularly flexible response from mental health professionals. In addition to this, they are not a group for whom there is likely to be a simple, effective therapeutic intervention. However, their vulnerability and the probable continuation of their problems into adult life if not helped early means that early intervention is vital. Some of the most damaged and difficult children receive no interventions and social services departments feel that they are left to cope without help from mental health agencies. It is the hallmark of quality services that they are able to take on the most challenging children and to continue to provide care and treatment. Services must find ways of coping with those who are already very damaged, who are likely to be difficult to engage, and for whom improvement will be slow and hard won.

Such intentions are dependent on good partnerships between social work professionals and the psychiatrists/psychologists responsible. However, it is clear that in practice such liaison is not taking place.

> "The key issue is the virtual total absence of input from relevant health specialists to diagnose and/or oversee the mental health of the children. Since very little is provided beyond an initial risk assessment by an adult forensic psychiatrist it would be difficult to say what is effective." [29]

There are examples of positive practice in this area, but yet again they appear to be only as a result of the vision and commitment of key individuals working in the field.

PARKVIEW CLINIC –
University of Birmingham, Department of Child and
Adolescent Psychiatry

Since August 1995, this service has been providing a 'direct access' mental health service to children in residential and foster care in Birmingham. The main aims of the service are to provide assessment and brief psychosocial interventions, as well as diversion to longer-term services where necessary. It also aims to provide support and advice for staff and families working with these youngsters. This includes help with foster parents.

By providing assessments on the mental health needs of these young people at the time of admission into care, it is hoped to facilitate other agencies involved in the young person's care plan. There is no waiting list for services, and referrals are made by the units or by other agencies involved. Young people are seen at the clinic, although they can be visited at the units if necessary. One weekly clinical session (four working hours) has been allocated to the intake unit because of its high turnover. The team also runs regular courses for residential care staff, social workers and foster carers on how to recognise and deal with child mental health problems.[30]

This was not the only example of positive work that we received. Brynffnnon Child and Family Service carries out strong liaison work with residential establishments looking after children. It tries to address the anomaly of the situation that is universal, ie the fact that the most disturbed children are looked after by the least trained professionals. They have been able to help a fair number of very disturbed youngsters through collaboration with residential establishments.[31]

We welcome the recognition through the recent *Quality Protects* initiative that the "mental health services for looked-after children are important and need improving", and that meeting the basic health needs of looked-after children has been identified as a priority in the National Priorities Guidance for 1999/2000.

A new target to ensure that all children are offered a comprehensive health assessment, and, where necessary, a treatment plan, on entry to the care system is an essential first step.

Recommendation: A key part of the service agreement of child and adolescent mental health services should be that they provide appropriate services for looked-after children.

Recommendation: We urge the Department of Health to ensure the implementation of the Health Committee's recommendation that named medical advisers should be responsible for the oversight of the mental health of each child in care and the Royal College of Nursing's recommendation that each residential home should have a named nurse, or that each home should be required to have formal links with local primary health care teams.

Recommendation: We support the Government's intention to make children's service planning a duty on local authorities as a whole, and the extension of local authorities' role to bring together agencies embracing children at risk of social exclusion.

"Listen to parents. They probably know their child and understand the problems. They may be in the best position to help the child...."

THE ROLE, VIEWS AND NEEDS OF PARENTS

"Parents need to be consulted, included in any decisions for their children's treatment, included in therapy and empowered to continue with their difficult task."

We received 204 submissions of written evidence from parents of children with mental health problems. Parents participating in the Inquiry in this way, were targeted primarily through their contact with mental health services, voluntary mental health organisations and support networks involved with carers for children with such problems as attachment disorder, attention deficit hyperactivity disorder, schizophrenia and eating disorders. A qualitative analysis of the written evidence was carried out, the results of which was produced into a supporting report.[32] The views of parents expressed throughout this report, and discussion below, draws upon this research, along with results from the focus groups with parents and the Search Conference held as part of the Inquiry.

Parents agree with professionals about the need for multidisciplinary services and shared professional training and wish to have an input into the way services are developed. Parents do not expect a gold standard service to be developed overnight. However, it is clear that from their experience there are key changes in the way parents are treated that are vital to a reasonable service:
- importance of being listened to and taken seriously
- provision of information
- importance of respite care/support for the family.

Importance of being listened to and taken seriously

"Parents and other immediate members could contribute greatly as they are the ones mostly affected by a member of a family who has a mental illness."

The importance of being listened to and taken seriously was one of the main themes to emerge in discussions with parents. They feel that they have a unique knowledge of their child to impart, which they often felt was not acknowledged by professionals. Many of the parents reported that, when they first approached professionals about their children's problems, they were often not taken seriously. They reported that they simply wanted their children's problems to be recognised and to be given guidance as to how best to treat and cope with whatever was wrong. Instead, their time and energy became divided between coping with the often extremely challenging behaviour of their children and engaging in 'running battles' to get themselves heard by professionals.

"I would have tried anything that may have improved the quality of my son's and, subsequently, our family life. Unfortunately, very little was forthcoming."

"In practical terms, we need very basic and obvious things like an understanding of the problem, a recognition of its seriousness, respite care at crisis point, and an approach that is not based on blaming either my daughter or myself for her distressing behaviour and obvious misery." [33]

When they tried to get help for their children, the experiences of the parents who responded to our questionnaire were almost universally negative. Before their children were diagnosed with mental health problems, most parents described a similar story; that of trying (often for years) to get health and social services to recognise, understand and treat effectively the difficulties that their children, and consequently the whole family, were experiencing. Most parents were understandably frustrated and angry at the length of time that this process had taken.[34]

"I seemed to bang my head on a brick wall; no one appeared to listen."

"If my eldest son had received help when he was five years old instead of when he was 15, I am sure he would have benefited and his confidence would not have been so badly damaged."

The evidence from parents suggests that there can be a conflict of interests between parents and professionals in relation to diagnosing problems. For the parents, a diagnosis seemed to serve as an empowering function, in that it at least confirmed their perceptions that something was wrong with their child.

"Diagnosis was helpful as it took the blame off us as parents."

Having a diagnosis seemed to enable parents to find information out for themselves, target specific services and ultimately communicate their needs better. However, for other parents, the period after initially gaining a diagnosis was experienced as being extremely distressing for both themselves and their children, such that they felt the need for support.

"You are expected to get on with it, without any real or meaningful support. No support to assist you over the shock of diagnosis."

It appeared that, for many parents, the importance placed on gaining a diagnosis was linked to the belief that this would enable them to gain access to help and support.

Most parents were concerned about the length of time their children had to wait before they were seen by services. Parents observed that in children, where emotional and psychological development is at a much faster rate than in adults, problems can rapidly escalate in the time it takes between getting a referral to, and actually being seen by, a particular agency.

"The wheels of bureaucracy turn so very slowly - too slowly to leave us with any quality of life."

"After a nearly two-year wait, we were told that they could teach us nothing new in our management strategies."

"As much as we understand that they need to make sure children get the right help, too much time is wasted while each child is assessed. Children need help now, not in 18 months time, it's too late for some children then."

Information and support

Two of the most frequent concerns in parents' evidence were those of not being given information regarding their child's illness by statutory services and the lack of support available for parents of children with mental health problems. The majority of parents found that it was only by seeking out information for themselves that they found out about particular disorders, treatment techniques and available support.[35]

"All the help we've received has been about how we can help our daughter. Which is valid and valuable, but the fact is we have felt and feel the need of help ourselves."

"I actually remember wishing my son had something like leukaemia instead of this. At least people would understand and care, and I would know what I was dealing with and get help quickly."

"He goes to another family for the weekend, it's fabulous. It's like his other family, they're like grandparents to him."

"Most parents at the 'end of their tether' tend to seek out information for themselves."

"The most help I've had in understanding schizophrenia has come from the National Schizophrenia Fellowship, local carers groups and the support of others in the same or similar situations."

Importance of respite care

When asked what would be the most important changes in services, after highlighting the need for more specialist help and support for their children, the majority of parents focused on the importance of some form of respite care for themselves and their other children.

"I've got to say this - what would have helped more than anything else would have been respite because nobody would mind this child, nobody wants them, nobody invites them anywhere, nobody helps you, as soon as they've had half an hour's experience of them they run a mile."

"It would have helped me a great deal, somebody to take [them] for a day, a weekend, you know, a week please! but, a day would have helped and that would have helped me to get calm, get my resources back, and then go in again, they do it for parents of disabled children, they should do it for us." [36]

The parents appeared to find the respite care offered by 'informal carers' particularly helpful.

Parents constantly expressed their sense of exhaustion and lack of support for themselves in their evidence to us. Where parents had gained access to support and self-help groups, they were unanimous in their praise of the support and information which they offered. Often such help appeared to be little more than a telephone help line, run by another mother in the area, and it is noteworthy that parents perceptions of these services – often run on a shoestring – were so much more positive than that of the professional help they were so desperate for.

Frustrations and praise

"Many parents praised individuals and services that had proved helpful, understanding and supportive. The praise, however, appeared more in the form of 'footnotes' to descriptions of services whose input had been perceived as far from ideal. It was unfortunate that the positive actions of the more effective individuals and services had been offset by the frustrations of the time it had taken parents to find and access them". [37]

The parents who responded to our questionnaire also expressed a great deal of anxiety about the future; not only for their own children, but for other children who may be suffering, unrecognised and untreated from mental health problems. They felt failed by the services, and also attacked, blamed and uncared for themselves. It was frequently only after much effort on their own part that parents had found services and individuals who were of help.

Recommendation: Parents of children experiencing mental health problems and young people must be consulted with and, where appropriate, involved in the development of services.

1 NHS Health Advisory Service (1996) *Together We Stand. Thematic Review on the commissioning role and management of child and adolescent mental health services* HMSO, London

2 Professional evidence to the Inquiry from a Health Trust

3 Professional evidence to the Inquiry from Social Services Authority

4 Professional evidence to the Inquiry

5 Professional evidence to the Inquiry

6 Wallace, S A Crown, J M Cox, A D Berger, M (1995) *Epidemiologically-based Needs Assessment; Child and Adolescent Mental Health* Wessex Institute of Public Health

7 Evidence to Inquiry from Dr Stephen Littlewood

8 Parent's evidence to the Inquiry

9 Parent from Cardiff focus group

10 Professional evidence to the Inquiry

11 NHS Exective, North West (1996) *Child and adolescent mental health: A review of services in the North West* NHS Executive, North West

12 Parent's evidence to the Inquiry

13 Parent's evidence to the Inquiry

14 Law, S (1998) *Hear Me* Mental Health Foundation, London

15 Wallace et al (1997) as in no 6

16 Kurtz, Z (1996) *Treating Children Well* Mental Health Foundation, London

17 Parent's evidence to the Inquiry

18 Professional evidence to the Inquiry

19 Evidence to the Inquiry from Royal College of Psychiatrists

20 Parent's evidence to the Inquiry

21 Parent from Cardiff Focus Group

22 Parent's evidence to the Inquiry

23 Professional evidence to the Inquiry

24 Professional evidence from the Bloomfield Centre, Guy's Hospital

25 O'Connell, P (1999) *Parent's evidence to the Inquiry* Mental Health Foundation, London (in press)

26 Parent's evidence to the Inquiry

27 Professional evidence from Professor Vostanis, University of Birmingham

28 Professional evidence to the Inquiry from Social Services Authority

29 Professional evidence to the Inquiry

30 Butler, J and Vostanis, P *Characteristics of referrals to a mental health service for young people in care* Psychiatric Bulletin in press June 1997

31 Professional evidence to the Inquiry

32 O'Connell, P (1999) as in no 25

33 Parent's evidence to the Inquiry

34 O'Connell, P (1999) as in no 25

35 O'Connell, P (1999) as in no 25

36 Parents at a focus group in Manchester

37 O'Connell, P (1999) as in no 25

Services for young people

" Young people with mental health problems need places to live where they have a degree of independence, but can be looked after when need be...."

INTRODUCTION

*" It should have been possible somehow to get him treatment....
before he became violent and involved with the court and police."*

The needs of 16-25 year-olds with mental health problems currently fall between child and adult services, especially in health and social services. Although much of what has been discussed in relation to children has relevance to young people, eg the role of schools, there is a clear need to focus on the specific needs of 16-25 year-olds in order to establish how those at risk can be reached. It can be inappropriate to target young people as members of their families because they are often trying to establish themselves as distinct individuals. They may not wish to share their difficulties with their families, or with professionals in touch with their parents. Young people are coping with the important transition to adulthood and autonomy, leaving school and entering further education, training or employment. Any approach to them must be based on an understanding of their lifestyles and networks.

This Chapter will consider what might promote the mental health and coping skills of young people; how young people might find help when they first experience problems or at crucial times, eg on leaving care or school. Evidence on services for those experiencing mental health difficulties will be discussed, based on written evidence from professionals, written evidence from young people, focus groups held with young people within a range of settings, discussions held with young people over a number of weekends, and a range of funded work consulting with young people. Alongside this, we will also briefly consider the needs of young offenders with mental health problems.

PROMOTION OF MENTAL HEALTH

We know from work on risk and resilience that there are important protective effects of having interests and hobbies, belonging to groups and organisations where adult role models will be present, and from specific adults who take an active interest in the young person's progress.

We also know that schools have a major contribution to make throughout the lives of young people, and evidence relating to young people again addressed the fear that pressure on schools to achieve academic success may affect their capacity to focus on the emotional development of pupils. The importance of school in the lives of children and young people was discussed in Chapters Two and Three. School will cease to be appropriate as a focus for some young people as they get older and they will need to be able to access services in the community which can promote their sense of inclusion and self-esteem.

Other important factors promoting the well-being of young people emerged from the evidence. In response to questions about how positive mental health could be achieved and maintained, young people in the Glasgow study and in focus and discussion groups relating to the Inquiry raised the following:

- the need for young people to feel safe, both physically and emotionally
- being able to talk to an adult of their choice in confidence – the young people's attitudes towards adults/professionals appears to be ambiguous, and despite the general feeling of the young people that they did not have access to professionals to whom they could talk, teachers were seen by some to be the most appropriate person to talk to about school-related issues, particularly bullying
- the need for sports centres and youth clubs which can provide interesting and meaningful activities "to keep us off the streets", and better and cheaper public transport so that they can access such provision.

We received a wealth of evidence from youth agencies working with young people on the potential of their service to promote young people's mental health.

"The work of youth services related to mental health can be located at two levels – the promotion of mental health at primary prevention level, in other words services and interaction with skilled youth workers can stop problems arising in the first place, eg young people learn to respect each other, work in groups, develop self-esteem and relationship skills and, at the secondary level, service intervention via the provision of advice and information (via Youth Information Shops) and counselling – which limits the development of difficulties into complex problems." [1]

Professionals and young people are agreed on the need for such universal provision and yet those submitting evidence drew our attention to a number of key factors which mean that its potential is seriously underdeveloped:

- the current variety, diversity and inconsistency of youth services provision both statutory and voluntary across the country
- the lack of a statutory base for the youth service which results in fragmentation
- the issue of funding, particularly that of issue-specific funding, which fails to recognise the primary prevention role of services and the holistic approach of youth work.

Recommendation: We recommend that, as part of the National Service Framework, a national strategy be developed on the mental health needs of young people (16-25) to ensure these are addressed as a priority.

Recommendation: The current inconsistency of youth service provision must also be resolved. It is vital that preventive services are given a clear statutory and funding basis.

EARLY INTERVENTION

Access to community-based services

The issue of most concern to the agencies submitting evidence was the need of young people for services and support which are appropriate for their age. Young people may present a wide variety of issues in a range of settings, schools, youth clubs, general practitioner practices, residential care, and it is vital that workers in these settings have the skills and support to work with young people adequately as a first 'port of call'. The consensus from the evidence was that community-based services are seen as the most 'young people friendly', both in terms of the services provided, and as a point of access into more specialist services where necessary.

"*Just knowing that you could pick up the phone and someone would be on the other end. They might not even understand, just listen to you.*" [3]

Many of the young people giving evidence stressed the lack of early help when first realising that they had a problem. Those general practitioners who had been responsive to the young people's needs were extremely highly praised.[2]

"*Great by the general practitioner. Brilliant – she will listen and talk to you. I must have had about 30 general practitioners and this is the best one I've had.*"

Unfortunately, for many young people their experiences of their general practitioner had been negative.

"*Waste of time. He didn't listen, he didn't have time to listen I should say. And he just put me on lots of tranquillisers.*"

The young people felt very strongly that general practitioners, if they were to be at all helpful for young people, should not only have increased training in mental health issues, but also in listening and communication skills. This view was reiterated by many of the professionals submitting evidence to the Inquiry. The work of many of the Youth Access counselling services was highlighted as being an especially useful source of unstigmatised help and support, as were many of the youth agencies working with young people, particularly those working with disadvantaged young people.

Agencies described accessible services as those which
• are able to respond flexibly to the needs of young people
• meet young people in their 'everyday environments'
• promote relationships with workers based on trust and respect outside of formal settings.

"Services that do not have an explicit 'mental' health/psychiatric label are less stigmatising. Early intervention and support can be effectively provided by non-medical staff, provided there is access to trained staff and specialist services where they are necessary." [4]

It is particularly important that such services are available for young people who are already disadvantaged and whose risk of developing mental health problems is therefore high. As the Base, a Barnados project working with disadvantaged young people in Whitley Bay stressed, "due to the chaos and movement in the young people's lives they regularly never get to specialist services and have many changes of workers or lie on waiting lists or have half-done assessments." [5]

Dalston Youth Project is an award-winning, intensive community-based mentoring and educational support programme for some of the most alienated young people in Hackney, aged 15-18. Through the support of a trained volunteer, mentor and an educational/vocational component, the young people, who may be involved in the criminal justice system or have been excluded from school, set personal goals and build their basic skills and self confidence, simultaneously decreasing the youth crime rate within the community.

The programme components include
- a rigorous recruitment and training process for volunteer mentors from the community
- recruitment of young people through statutory and local agencies
- two residential programmes, outside London, for up to 20 young people and 25 volunteers, helping the young people begin to set realistic goals for themselves
- weekly mentoring meetings, with one young person and one volunteer
- monthly support group meetings and surgeries for the volunteer mentors
- an eight-week educational and vocational programme (College Taster Course) for the young people, designed in collaboration with Hackney Community College
- on-going, on-site career and educational activities
- pre-employment training programme.

Problems experienced by youth services

"Voluntary counselling services have developed on an ad hoc, piecemeal basis. In the absence of a national strategy to respond to young people's information, advice and counselling needs, this had led to uneven levels and distribution of services, together with variability in skills levels held within services. In addition, a disproportionate amount of time is spent by many of the voluntary services in managing funding crises – all too often these services have been seen as marginal activities. As a consequence, young people's ability to access services depends entirely on where they live." [6]

The National Youth Agency sees the key constraints in services for young people as being
- the lack of a statutory base for the youth service, which leads to fragmentation and inconsistency
- the real need for an Adolescent Health Commissioner, working across health and local authority provision, with some responsibility for coordination across acute, primary care and prevention
- the marginalisation of the youth service when it comes to debates related to suicide, depression, exclusion, truancy and teenage pregnancy – youth work approaches would have much to offer within formal educational settings and prevention initiatives.

Funding is widely recognised as a major constraint for youth agencies, not simply the lack of funding, but the lack of any ownership of responsibility for funding and the issue-based funding which leaves core project costs unfunded and constantly threatens continuity of service. Voluntary sector organisations operate at the interface between statutory agencies, often across age and need boundaries, and include those who do not fit into other services. If staff are to provide secure and empowering services, they need to have some stability of funding. Joint planning and funding can provide that secure basis and ensure better integration of services.

Recommendation: We add our voice to those of others that there needs to be a national underpinning of the role and structure of the youth service.

Recommendation: There must be clear responsibility at a local level for the development of services for vulnerable young people which are fully coordinated across the tiers.

Young people leaving care

The Children Act 1989 imposes a duty on local authorities in respect of care leavers.

> *"Where a child is being looked after by a local authority, it shall be the duty of the authority to advise, assist and befriend him with a view to promoting his welfare when he ceases to be looked after by them."* [7]

Local authorities also have the power to provide assistance in cash or kind to young people who have left care, and to assist with education, employment or training up to age of 21 (or, in the case of young people in full-time education, until they finish that education). These powers were envisaged as being consistent with the responsibilities of the local authority as a 'good parent' to the young people; with a good parent offering support to his or her children throughout the potentially difficult period of leaving home and establishing an independent life. This period in the young person's life has clearly important implications in relation to promoting mental health.

The main issues which put young care leavers at risk are
- the early age of independence in comparison with other non-care young people – the average age of young people leaving care is 16-18
- the low educational attainment, poor careers and early parenthood of young people leaving care
- the lack of financial support, life skills and support in gaining and maintaining accommodation, resulting in the overrepresentation of young care leavers who are homeless.

> *"The evidence from [these studies] shows that young people leaving care have to cope with the challenges and responsibilities of major changes in their lives – in leaving residential and foster care and setting up home, in leaving school and entering the world of work or, more likely, being unemployed and surviving on benefits, and in being parents at a far younger age than other young people. In short, they have compressed and accelerated transitions to adulthood."* [8]

The Government has recognised the vulnerability of young people on leaving care, and the current lack of consistency in services for this group through its *Quality Protects* initiative. Of particular importance in relation to promoting the mental health of young people living away from home are the proposals to
- amend the powers currently held within Section 24 of the Children Act into a duty for young people up to 18 – we would of course recommend that this duty is extended to young people aged up to 21
- monitor the discharge of young people from care at 16, in order to maximise the number of young people leaving care after their 16th birthday who are still in touch with the social services department, or a known and approved contact on their 19th birthday.

We know from research that 'leaving care' schemes are effective in supporting young people through this difficult period. [9] The importance of practical skills training has been highlighted as being key to young people's well-being. In a study of preparation for leaving care in Norfolk, young people saw practical skills and the participatory way in which they were taught as key. In addition to their need for skills training, young people leaving care are socially isolated, often dependent on professionals for support [10] and it is therefore vital that 'leaving care' schemes also facilitate young people in developing friendship and social networks. Those working with young care leavers need to have specialist knowledge of local youth and leisure provision, in order to be able to plug young people into that provision, as well as providing their own groups and drop-in facilities.

The importance, however, of young people being able to maintain relationships with significant adults in their lives cannot be underestimated. As Stein said, "perhaps the key to successful outcomes lay with young people having positive, supportive relationships with family members or former foster carers". Information, advice and counselling services can play a useful role during this transition, especially if they target an age range up to 25. As social services and leaving care schemes tail off, young people in contact with these services are able to maintain another source of support. This highlights the importance of services that cross age barriers, especially for those whose development is affected by adverse life experiences.

Recommendation: We recommend that the new arrangements proposed by the Government in relation to 16-18 year-olds in care, which are aimed at developing their life skills and clarifying the responsibilities for their financial support, should be extended to young people up to 21.

We welcome the increasing emphasis on the corporate responsibility of the local authority as a whole to improve the full range of services for looked-after children and other vulnerable children and young people. Of particular importance is the stronger role for Children's Services Plans in order to make them a more effective instrument of corporate working.

Recommendation: Accessible, mainstream youth services, targeted at vulnerable groups, should be provided, with additional, specialist support and advocacy services for young people who have been looked after.

Young people, alcohol and drugs

According to the British Youth Council, young people are the heaviest drinkers and smokers in the population. In addition, between a quarter and a third will have tried solvents or illegal drugs by the time they are 20.[11]

Among young people alcohol is the drug most commonly used at both legal and illegal ages.[12] There is a clear relationship between smoking, drinking alcohol and experimentation with drugs. The Health Education Authority's survey of school children aged 11-16 found that young people who smoked, drank alcohol or had tried drugs were less likely to assess themselves as 'very healthy' and more likely to suffer symptoms of both physical and mental ill health.

The relationship between alcohol and drug abuse and mental health problems is not simple, but alcohol and/or drug abuse is a risk factor for developing mental health problems, and young people experiencing mental health problems can become dependent on alcohol or drugs. In the UK, the number of people suffering from both a severe mental health illness and alcohol/drug misuse appears to be high.[13] Research comparing people with a dual diagnosis (ie psychosis and substance misuse) and those with a psychosis only, have found that those with a dual diagnosis are typically young people, more often male and at risk of homelessness.

Evidence suggests that young people experiencing both mental health problems and alcohol/drug dependency are particularly vulnerable.

"This group of young people are especially vulnerable. Their needs are multiple and complex. The kinds of problem we see are homelessness, family dysfunction, sexual abuse, prostitution, deliberate self-harm, depression and anxiety, psychotic episodes, truancy, unemployment, school exclusion and crime." [14]

The evidence further suggests that the needs of this group are not being met. The issues which were highlighted as being particularly problematic were

- the use of school exclusion as a response to substance misuse in children
- the inappropriateness of adult drug/alcohol services for young people
- the fragmentation of available services, particularly education, social services, health, police and probation and voluntary organisations
- the lack of attention by mental health services to the needs of young people with drug or alcohol dependency
- those services which do exist have developed in an isolated, uneven, patchy and idiosyncratic manner.

This is not an area which we examined in detail and is clearly an area where further work needs to be carried out. We would want to support the recommendations highlighted in the HAS Thematic Review: *Children and Young People Substance Misuse Services*. In particular

- the implementation of the four-tiered model as set out in *Together We Stand*
- the development of an accurate knowledge base about the problems and issues
- an overarching commissioning strategy that takes account of the local needs and seeks specific standards of service from a mix of provider services
- appropriate training for key staff
- mechanisms for creating integrated programmes of care for individuals that recognise the importance of care pathways and the role and patterns of shared care involving direct access and specialist services
- the development of more effective and appropriate substance misuse services for children and adolescents should become a major item on the agenda of all health authorities.

Many young people will have been exposed to the negative effects on family relationships as a result of their parents' drug or alcohol problems. It is important that those services catering for adults also take account of the young people in the family and link them in to appropriate sources of help, advice and support. This means having links with social services, youth agencies, child and adolescent mental health services, and having staff who are able to relate to the young people and facilitate a referral.

ALCOHOL SERVICES IN CHESHIRE

This young people's project focuses partly on young people's drinking and partly on their parents' drinking. The project works with schools, the Youth Service, drop-in health clinics and in other places where young people are likely to go. The project also employs a women's outreach worker who will visit mothers who have alcohol problems.

The work of the project has resulted in there being a network of agencies which are aware of the problem of drinking parents, and that schools and youth agencies are becoming increasingly expert at identifying young people in difficulty and using specialist services. Funding for this comes in part from the Single Regeneration Budget, since South Cheshire is seen as being economically disadvantaged, the rest from health and local authorities, both of which are committed to providing this kind of service.

Recommendation: Joint planning structures, and arrangements for interagency working must take account of young people in families where parents have problems. Children's Services Plans and joint planning groups could play an essential role – for example child and adolescent mental health services can have a useful input into substance misuse services, but are unlikely to do so unless the planning system supports this.

SERVICES FOR YOUNG PEOPLE EXPERIENCING MENTAL HEALTH DIFFICULTIES

Responsive services

We heard from young people how hard it was for them to find their way into services and how often, when they finally gained access to help, they found themselves confronted by professionals who appeared to be both disinterested and intrusive. Many described how difficult they had found being expected to talk about deeply distressing incidents after only a couple of meetings with the psychiatrists/psychologists and how these professionals appeared to be unresponsive to their needs.

In contrast to this, many spoke highly of those professionals who had reached out to them.

"Sound. The psychologist came and took me for days out and did things with me. Sat down and talked to me, put me on a special diet."

"They were great, I really felt that they cared about me, took the time to find out who I was – you know, not just a number like the rest of them."

The responsiveness of the professionals they came into contact with was a major factor in determining how young people and their parents felt about the service they received. Where professionals were felt to be patronising, to be unwilling to share information with the young people about their illnesses, or appeared not to have any time for the young person, they in turn felt let down by the treatments on offer. A number spoke of the need for psychiatrists in particular to be "less bow-tie and more youth worker".

It is clear that a great deal could be done to transform young people's experience of services if professionals were trained in listening empathetically to young people and were able to have a more flexible response to meeting young people in more informal settings.

Where services are designed to be responsive to young people's needs, the results are extremely impressive.

"I needed some help straight away – not to delve into my past which made me feel worse."

This is a voluntary sector project in Manchester providing a range of community-based services for young people who are experiencing a wide range of mental health problems. The project offers individual work in the form of counselling, informal support and befriending relationships. Alongside this, they offer an extensive group work programme which includes a weekly drop-in group, suicide/self-harm group, and groups for young lesbians, gay men and bisexuals.

Within its overall brief of meeting the needs of young people within a broad youth work philosophy, the development of distinctive projects with a particular focus has lead to a number of important developments:

- the establishment of links by the suicide and self-harm project with the accident and emergency departments has led to clear improvements in the service that young people receive at this point of crisis, and the development of accessible community-based group work provision for young people around these issues
- the lesbian, gay and bisexual project has highlighted the particular mental health difficulties experienced by some gay people – all too often overlooked by existing mental health provision
- provision of a three-year programme of education work in schools and youth clubs led to the development of mental health preventive strategies and initiatives, and the forthcoming production of a mental health education pack and related materials.

Such services are operating across the formal tiered structure of mental health services, offering direct access services to young people alongside services for young people with profound mental health problems. Both 42nd Street and SAFE, whilst offering specialist therapeutic help, are also offering a range of more community-based services.

"We are offering therapy for mental illness, but also working on alienation – giving young people a place to belong."[15] It is clear that a great deal of innovative work could be carried out with young people by creating partnerships between existing services which are working with young people in a 'holistic way' and specialists in child and adolescent mental health.

"Services that operate on a nine-to-five and appointment basis are fairly inaccessible for young people. They do not take the chaotic nature of their lives into account. Flexible services that operate in the evening and on a drop-in basis seem to have greater success of building up relationships with young people sufficient for them to want to or be able to manage an appointment." [16]

In return, many voluntary sector initiatives spoke of their need for input from specialist services. Indeed, effective relationships with more specialist services are the key to the successful development of these cross-tier services. Croydon Youth Counselling, an agency with tiers two and three status and funding from the Department of Health, provides a useful model in how to develop such services.

"The voluntary sector model of youth counselling provision appears to be particularly effective in meeting a range of young people's needs. We are able to offer a flexible response to complex issues in a setting which does not stigmatise young people. This also enables us to reach young people who are suspicious of statutory services. One example of this is that we have recently appointed an ethnic minorities outreach worker who will be building links with young people from different ethnic minority communities to raise awareness of the statutory and voluntary sector services available and to encourage these young people to use and become involved in the future planning and delivery of mental health services." [17]

SAFE

The Service for Adolescents and Families in Enfield (SAFE) is a community-based adolescent service. It is provided by Enfield Community Care National Health Service Trust, in collaboration with the Education Group of the local authority, via the Enfield Child Guidance Service.

The project was set up to provide community-based rapid and intensive assessment and intervention with adolescents suffering from or at risk of mental health crisis or family breakdown. The project has been delivered by a multidisciplinary team of mental health care professionals, including a psychiatrist, a clinical psychologist, a child and adolescent psychotherapist, part-time educational psychologist and two family therapists/social workers. The project currently offers a day service, and is planning to develop a small in-patient facility: a four to six bed unit attached to the paediatric ward. The multidisciplinary team is a collaboration between ECCT and the Education Group of the local authority (Child Guidance).

Evidence has been collected by the project which demonstrates that
- the service has been utilised from across the local authority
- adolescents from all secondary schools in the area have used the service
- referrals have come from a wide and appropriate range of sources
- the service is reaching the target group by age and diagnosis.

As SAFE's own report on its progress said, "SAFE is making a major contribution to the Health of the Nation target for reducing suicides (a reduction in rates of parasuicide in the under 16 Enfield population presenting at Chase Farm Hospital from 43 in 92/93 down to 29 in 96/97)". Evidence also demonstrated that
- there has been a reduction in ECRs
- there has been a positive response to the service from referrers and clients
- patients are seen quickly
- about two or three are seen for fewer than eight sessions.

The project sees itself as complementing the work carried out in the Child Guidance Centres, with particularly difficult clients/patients, thus allowing the Child Guidance Service to devote their time to developing and providing an appropriate services for the other children and families with mental health needs. They are able to provide more support to the paediatric ward in relation to teenagers admitted after self-harm or with eating disorders, or with severe mental illness. They are also better able to support the work of the Adult Mental Health Unit in teenager patients who have been referred to them.

"Young people like to access the service on their own territory, they like the informality and they do go on to use our central service to follow up on issues." [18]

Recommendation: Within the National Service Framework, there should be a strategy on the mental health needs of young people to address
- the funding and location of preventive work with young people ensuring that innovative models of practice gain access to appropriate long-term funding
- the promotion of effective practice in meeting the needs of young people
- ways and settings which young people find acceptable
- ensuring that services for young people are operating across tiers
- access to specialist support and supervision from mental health services for community-based services working with vulnerable young people
- the gap between child and adults' services
- specialist services, eg for eating disorders and young people who self-harm.

Developing appropriate services for young people will clearly present many challenges, particularly in relation to the location of services, professional approaches, attitudes and training, and the challenge for many of forging new ways of working with other agencies and tiers and with young people themselves.

> "I was really scared, 'cause it was full of old people rocking and making noises and that, and I thought – is that how I'm going to end up, is that what's going to happen to me – and it just sort of made me feel worse." [19]

Lack of specialist provision

The lack of specialist provision, across the whole spectrum of child and adolescent mental health services, is felt particularly acutely by young people currently caught between services for children and those for adults. The problems affecting this group (16-25 year olds) have also been highlighted by previous reports and both *Bridges Over Troubled Water* and the HAS report *Together We Stand* recommended that there be a specialist young people's service developed for this age group. This lack of provision was highlighted as an area of concern by a majority of those submitting evidence to us.

We heard of many examples of positive work with young people with severe mental health problems:
- specialist adolescent/young people's day units which are providing an important integrated service to young people
- specialist in-patient units where specifically trained staff are able to offer a range of interventions to young people
- innovative voluntary sector initiatives which, whilst offering help and support to young people with severe mental health problems, are able to do so in an open and informal setting.

However, all too often, we were also presented with clear gaps in the services available. Young people spoke of their difficulty in gaining access to specialist help.

> "The waiting list gets me – wait all the time. I was on a waiting list for a year or so when I was 17, and I was 18 when they got round to it – to see a consultant psychiatrist. In the end I went to a general practitioner and refused to move... saw the understudy and then the consultant."

The lack of specialist in-patient provision for young people is an issue of major concern. A particular problem is that of young people placed on adult wards as the only provision available in their area, an experience which was described as being frightening and disorientating by the young people.

The impact of lack of resources on the delivery of services to young people was highlighted by a number of those submitting evidence.

The particular gaps highlighted include
- an inability to respond to emergency referrals
- the lack of secure or intensive care facilities to provide safe environments and therapeutic care for the most vulnerable young people, including young offenders with mental health problems
- the need for more adolescent in-patient units
- the lack of funding preventing an adequate duration of treatment
- units for young people with specific problems, ie young people with eating disorders
- further day unit provision in accessible community locations.

The creation of a separate service for young people as recommended by *Bridges Over Troubled Water* has much to commend it. However, it could also result in the creation of a new set of service boundaries which will need to be negotiated by professionals, parents and young people. Whatever structure is finally deemed most appropriate, priority must be given to the needs of young people experiencing mental health problems.

In-patient services

The Report to the Health Select Committee by the Association of Adolescent Psychiatrists estimated that about 210 (30%) in-patient adolescent beds had closed during the 1980s. Although new units had opened in some regions there had been a net loss in beds nationally. We have already highlighted the distressing experience for young people of their admission to adult wards. Whilst many young people who gave evidence were highly critical of their treatment within in-patient provision, a significant number were impressed by the level of support that they were offered. For them, their time on an adolescent ward appears to have given them an important space away from the other stresses and strains of their lives.

> *"Young people's accounts paint a complex picture of the value of residential facilities. None of the young people approached the possibility of hospitalisation with a light heart, and many were clearly distressed and anxious at the prospect. The majority do, however, appear to feel that they derived real benefits from both the 'sanctuary' from everyday stresses (particularly family and school) and from the, albeit enforced, proximity to other young people in similar circumstances to their own."* [20]

What appeared to make this experience positive for the young people was the quality of the relationships they were able to form with those around them, and time and time again, it was those professionals who related to the young people 'on the level' who were the most trusted.

"They explained things and I thought it was good, instead of just giving you tranquillisers and stuff, if you were anxious or anything they make you work through the anxiety. They wouldn't just give you a tablet to get rid of the anxiety, you have to tell them how you're feeling, and get rid of it like that, and anxiety management and stuff like that." [21]

These relationships are, however, in direct contrast to the often very negative experiences that other young people recounted of their experiences on psychiatric wards. Many felt that they had been given medication, 'chemical cosh', inappropriately, with very little information about what they were taking or what its effects would be, and little choice concerning the treatments that they were offered.

Another area of concern for young people in relation to in-patient treatment was the issue of their discharge. Many felt that they were not adequately prepared for leaving the hospital – and that services did not take into account the situation into which young people were going. A number of the young people giving evidence to the Inquiry were faced with extremely insecure housing, and potential homelessness on leaving hospital, yet felt that they were given little support in resolving their situation. From the stories recounted by young people of their experiences on leaving hospital, it is clear that they feel they get insufficient support. This could be remedied by positive outreach and building community-based support for young people before they are discharged. The young people questioned the abrupt cutting off of contact with professionals with whom they have built up relationships in hospital. Given the importance of the relationship with these hospital-based staff, consideration should be given to their being able to provide some follow-up until care has been handed over to community staff.

Recommendation: The practice of placing young people under 18 on adult wards must cease, and greater care should be given to the provision of appropriate in-patient provision for under 25 year-olds.

Young offenders

Although it is known that young offenders are at high risk of developing mental health problems, their needs are currently being shamefully overlooked.

> *"Mental health problems, both in young offenders and older offenders, represent the single area of most concern in the available literature. The findings of an overall association between mental health problems and offending in young people are variable from different studies in different countries. However, most, especially those from the UK, conclude that the prevalence of mental health problems is increased amongst young offenders before, during and following incarceration. The most obvious and serious example of this is demonstrated by the high rates of suicide or attempted suicide amongst young offenders."* [22]

> *"Research has shown that mental health and emotional difficulties are major problems for young people in prisons; over 50% of remanded young males and 30% of sentenced young males have a diagnosable mental disorder."* [23]

Despite this, only one young offender establishment in England and Wales did a psychiatrist interview with all new receptions. There also appeared to be great difference between establishments in the numbers of young prisoners referred to visiting psychiatrists.[24]

Suicide and self-harm in custody

One of the major areas of concern for us is the numbers of young people in custody who self-harm or who are at risk of suicide. The Howard League's evidence to the Inquiry showed a suicide rate amongst young people on remand three times that of the general population in custody.[25] HM Chief Inspector's *Thematic Review of Younger Prisoners* found that in 1996/7, the number of young prisoners who had taken their own life had doubled since the previous year. The Inspector himself described the situation as being alarming.

> *"There is insufficient understanding and awareness in recognising the mental health concerns of young people amongst community and custodial agencies. It is alarming that the problem is not being urgently addressed, because of the consequences both to the individual and the community."* [26]

It has been suggested that one of the key problems is the lack of beds within the National Health Service for young offenders. There is also the potential for disagreement over the level of security needed in National Health Service care, resulting in young people being passed between clinicians – all recommending each other's service. Whilst we would support the view that young people who require specialist mental health services should come under the remit of the National Health Service, there is a great deal that could be done to improve the ethos and culture within prisons in order to protect vulnerable young people from the risks to their mental health they are currently experiencing.

Given the pervasiveness of bullying in the prison system, full and effective antibullying measures should underpin the entire way in which any prison or young offender establishment is run, in order to prevent abusive behaviour and its impact on the mental health of vulnerable young people.

Comprehensive coordinated information on children and young people arriving at young offender institutes or prison should be available. There is often no information about the (alleged) offence, no details in relation to previous convictions or the background of the young people and their mental health history, thus preventing a proper risk or needs assessment being made.

We heard that effective first night arrangements and ongoing support for new and inexperienced prisoners can significantly reduce the risks of self-harm or suicide. Routines and support should be in place to identify, assist and support young people who have been exposed to sexual, physical or emotional abuse. In order to facilitate this, it is vital for prisons to gain the benefit of a multiagency approach, with clear links being made with local mental health, social work and probation agencies. All establishments holding children should be linked to their Area Child Protection Committee – to develop appropriate protocols and multiagency approaches to young people who have been sexually, physically or emotionally abused.

There is, of course, a whole range of difficulties manifested by young people in custody, and the prison health care service currently lacks the skills and facilities to respond effectively to meet children/young people's needs. The great majority of young prisoners do not meet the requirements for transfer to the National Health Service facilities (under Mental Health Act 1983) and require treatment in prison. However, we heard disturbing evidence concerning the lack of services for children and young people experiencing severe mental health problems. There is rarely input from specialist mental health professionals and we heard that the culture within many prison health centres is often unsympathetic.

"Currently, standards of health care are characterised by poor facilities and the absence of a culture in which young prisoners are treated as patients."

"Too many health care staff are drawn into preoccupations with 'weeding out' those perceived to be manipulators of the system." [27]

We also heard examples of extremely positive practice in relation to joint working between prisons and child and adolescent mental health services in order to provide specialist multidisciplinary care for young people in custody.

> *"We work closely with Colvin Unit at St Nicholas Hospital, Gosforth. They have a six bed forensic adolescent unit, we have a package from them which provides us with a Consultant Adolescent Psychiatrist, Clinical Psychologist and CPNs. One of this team comes to our health centre daily, Monday to Friday. Our own staff consist of a collection of RGNs and RMNs."* [28]

We welcome the Government's commitment to the creation of a distinct estate within the Prison Service for 15-17 year olds, and the commitment to improving the care and regimes delivered within it. Within this, we would want to ensure that those recommendations made by HM Chief Inspector's *Thematic Review of Young Prisoners* are fully implemented.

Recommendation: We believe that attention must be urgently given to the mental health needs of young people in young offender institutes and in prisons.
- Full initial assessments must be carried out on all young people. Those young prisoners who arrive with warnings concerning their vulnerability, or who exhibit these signs to reception staff, should be dealt with as a priority.
- For those young people who require it, the full range of services should be made available from trained mental health nurses, clinical psychologists, occupational therapists and others who form part of the normal mental health care team within the National Health Service.

In addition to this, we recommend that
- the Youth Justice Board should become the commissioning authority for all custodial provision for those under 18 (as the Government has suggested)
- the Board should require the operators to work to clear standards of provision and performance, based on the Children Act and the UN Convention and at least equivalent to those of the NHS in matters of health care and treatment
- young offender institutions should be inspected by joint teams with membersfrom each of the relevant professions, reporting to the Youth Justice Board. These institutions should as soon as practicable be removed from the Prison Service and the prisons estate, and be placed under separate, specialised management with suitable mechanisms of accountability.

The Howard League report[29] found that local authority secure accommodation provided "much higher standards of supervision and care than the prison system". Problems of bullying and self-harm were identified, but "the major area of concern is the lack of properly trained staff". As with other issues relating to staff training, we would want to see these addressed in the context of a wider strategy to address the training needs of professionals working with young people in relation to mental health issues. We identified secure accommodation for young people, including youth treatment centres, as an area for the future, but recommend that the Howard League report be followed up.

COMPONENTS OF A GOOD MENTAL HEALTH SERVICE

Young people had clear ideas about what makes up an effective and accessible mental health service.

Somewhere for young people to go during the day
"Drop-in centres, talking treatments, art therapy, drama therapy, other alternative therapies instead of drugs, just drugs."

A 24 hour helpline
"A 24-hour mental health helpline, a centre for young people 24-hours a day, seven days a week and support groups in every town/city."

"A 24-hour phone line with qualified counsellors. Young people would feel more confident if they felt that there was someone to whom they could talk who was 'qualified' and who has experience." [30]

Better out-of-hours services
"How one is treated in moments of crisis is very important in forming a person's view of a service. For young people to experience repeated failures to offer appropriate help must reinforce their sense of desperation. There will always be some young people who need help out of hours, and services need to rethink how they respond to these situations." [31]

Mental health advocates for young people
"A mental health advocate would take a lot of the fear away. Someone who was telling you the facts. They would have a link with you and at least you would have one contact person and build up trust and a follow-up system for a set time."

Other components
- An holistic approach, starting 'where the young person is at'.
- Seeing someone immediately who can provide some service and explore other issues.
- A service provided in a young person-friendly environment which does not label young people as having a particular problem, eg mental health or drugs. For all young people to be able to access the service, but for the work to be targeted at the most needy.
- For the service to be open access and provide a continuum of services from practical help, such as food and the use of a phone, to more complex emotional support.
- To be given clear information and choice with medication.
- Having a say in how mental health services are run.

The agencies giving evidence to us accorded with these views and again stressed
- the importance of practical help for young people, whether in relation to support for young people leaving care, support with accommodation and benefits for young homeless people, practical support for young people on being discharged from hospital, or practical help, such as phoning general practitioners and contacting appropriate agencies for young people attending youth counselling services
- the importance of young people being listened to – time and someone to talk to
- the value of paying close attention to equal opportunities and antidiscriminatory practice in the provision of wide-ranging services
- the development of participatory structures which enable young people to influence services.

Developing appropriate services for young people will clearly present many challenges for existing services, particularly in relation to the location of services, professional approaches, attitudes and training, and the challenge for many of forging new ways of working with other agencies and tiers, and with young people themselves.

Recommendation: We recommend as a priority for further work on services for young people
- the development, evaluation and promotion of examples of innovative practice
- a commitment to long-term core funding of those services which can demonstrate effectiveness
- the development of a national strategy for the training of professionals working with young people.

1 Professional evidence to the Inquiry

2 Young people's focus group

3 Laws, S (1999) *Time to Listen* Save The Children

4 Professional evidence to the Inquiry

5 Professional evidence to the Inquiry

6 Professional evidence to the Inquiry

7 Children Act 1989, Section 24(1)

8 Stein, M (1997) *What Works in leaving care?* Barnardos, Essex

9 Biehal, N Clayden, J Stein, M Wade, J (1995) *Moving On: Young people and leaving care schemes* HMSO, London

10 Stein, M (1997) as in no 8

11 *Never Had It So Good? The Truth About Being Young in 90s Britain* British Youth Council and Barnardos 1996

12 Department of Health (1992) *The Health of the Nation* HMSO, London Royal College of Physicians, British Paediatric Association (1995) *Alcohol and Young People* (1995)

13 Gournay, K Sandford, T Johnson, S Thornicroft, G (1997) *Dual Diagnosis of severe mental health problems and substance abuse/dependence: a major priority for mental health nursing* Journal of Psychiatric and Mental Health Nursing 4 pp89-95
National Schizophrenia Fellowship fact sheet 7 NSF, London

14 Professional evidence to the Inquiry

15 Professional evidence from Tony Kaplan, Consultant Psychiatrist at SAFE

16 Professional evidence to the Inquiry

17 Professional evidence to the Inquiry

18 Professional evidence to the Inquiry

19 Young person's focus group

20 White, S (1998) *In their own words: young people's accounts of their experiences as users of child and adolescent mental health services* in Stockport University of Manchester/Stockport Joint Commissioning Group for Child and Adolescent Mental Health, Stockport

21 Laws, S (1999) as in no 3

22 Marcfarlane A (1997) *Literature Review on the health of young people between 16-24 detained in young offender units or prisons in England and Wales* in *Young Prisoners: A Thematic Review by HM Chief Inspector of Prisons for England and Wales* HMSO, London

23 HM Inspectorate of Prisons for England and Wales (1997) *Young Prisoners: A Thematic Review by HM Chief Inspector of Prisons for England and Wales* HMSO, London p50

24 Kurtz, Z Thornes, R and Bailey, S (1997) *Children in the criminal justice systems: how their mental health needs are met* Journal of Adolescence vol 21 pp543-553

25 Grindrod, H and Black, G (1989) *Suicides at Leeds Prison: An enquiry into the deaths of five teenagers during 1988/89* Howard League, London

26 HM Inspectorate of Prisons for England and Wales (1997) as in no 22

27 HM Inspectorate of Prisons for England and Wales (1997) as in no 22

28 Professional evidence to the Inquiry

29 *Banged Up, Beaten Up, Cutting Up* Report of the Howard League Commission of Inquiry into Violence in Penal Institutions for teenagers under 18

30 Presentation to the Inquiry from young people from 42nd Street

31 Law, S (1998) *Hear Me* Mental Health Foundation, London

The way forward

INTRODUCTION

"Society therefore has a choice whether to acknowledge the importance of the mental health of its children and invest in it appropriately or not... if we are to change things action is needed now." [1]

It is clear from all the evidence considered in this report that mental health in children is inextricably linked to the whole of their lives. The chances of developing into a mentally healthy, emotionally stable, coping adult are seriously impaired by social adversity, poor parenting, low intelligence, poor achievement, impoverished social networks and threatening life events. Indeed, those risk factors themselves expose children to more adverse life events.[2] Understanding this has major implications not only for delivery of services, but for policy-making in the very widest sense.

As well as an understanding of what predisposes someone to mental health problems (and indeed to other adverse outcomes) there is an accumulating body of evidence as to what the protective factors are and how children can acquire the necessary resilience. However, the very broad range of the risk factors, which include such basic factors as poverty, means that a multifactorial approach to combating their effects is vital. Delivering individual interventions to individual children will be only one small part of tackling this problem. There will be implications across the whole structure of society if a programme to create healthy children is to be implemented.

In this final Chapter we will look at the changes which may help to promote a mentally healthy environment for children. The implications of recent relevant initiatives and their interrelationship will be discussed. Proposals for the harmonisation of legislation and guidance and some possible changes in government structure will be presented as a further contribution to the debate. Likewise, the implications for local changes, especially in interagency working, will be set out. After consideration of further work arising from this Inquiry, a summary of recommendations for national, local, organisational and professional change will be presented.

THE CURRENT CONTEXT

This report has shown how specialist services are patchy, under-funded and plagued by lack of coordination and discontinuities between agencies. We were not surprised that the lack of resources should have been a persistent complaint from many of those who gave evidence to this Inquiry, or that many practitioners should perceive it as having an inhibiting effect both on the exercise of their professional skills and on their own commitment and enthusiasm. It would have been possible for us to draw up a list of demands for extra resources, which we would have considered to be entirely justified and supported by the evidence that we found. We are not, however, so naive as to suppose that such a list would be considered politically or economically acceptable, or that the relevant authorities would necessarily be able to spend extra funds to good effect, even if they became immediately available. We are also conscious that many of the frustrations which practitioners and interest groups attribute to the lack of resources have their origins in the circumstance in which they work – failures of understanding or communication, lack of trust in working relationships, a defensive attitude towards protecting a service's territory, perverse incentives or discouragements created by a service's funding mechanisms or performance indicators. These problems are systemic and structural, rather than personal or individual. It has become clear through the course of our work that skills and knowledge must be 'pushed down' to those who are engaged on a day to day basis with children, young people and their families, just as the lessons from their practice, particularly those around effective consultations, partnership and community empowerment, must be taken on board by those in running and developing specialist services.

We have formed what we believe to be a coherent vision of the kind of provision we would like to see made for promoting the mental health of children and young people, and we hope we can communicate that vision through this report. We would also like to see a systematic programme, with target dates, for making that provision available on the ground, but we accept that it is more realistic at this stage to focus not only on the outcomes, but also on the processes by which they can be achieved. We have therefore included a number of legislative, structural and procedural recommendations with the hope that they will help to create the conditions in which those outcomes can be achieved. We also hope that they will help to generate the human resources of commitment and will, and of energy and understanding, which are needed to ensure that physical and financial resources are used to the best possible effect.

There are signs that the current government is beginning to acknowledge the need for government departments to work together to address at least some of these issues, although some inconsistencies are still evident. The emphasis on social exclusion, families, children under eight and children in care all have implications across health, education, social service, the criminal justice system and beyond that to policies on housing, employment and taxation.

In the last year, a range of initiatives or prototypes have been developed by government to promote action on preventive services and on interventions that rely on agency collaboration, adopting a more holistic approach, eg health improvement programmes, *Health Action Zones*, *Education Action Zones*, the *Sure Start* initiative, *New Deal for Communities*, etc. They are all projects that address some of the issues and recommendations in the report. Although widely welcomed, these initiatives are not without problems.

A major difficulty facing these initiatives is whether they can work within the present structures, guidance, legislation and funding regimes or whether these need changing to enable these new ventures to have a better chance of success. Most involve collaboration between, at the very least, health, education and social services for initial bidding success and will depend for long-term success on more long-lasting collaboration. Some early successes may be attributable to the 'Hawthorne' or experimental effect where enthusiastic pioneers collaborate, win their bids for eg *Health Action Zone* monies, but where success for the second and third wave is increasingly difficult to replicate. These initiatives deserve to be rigorously evaluated. The successful replication of and learning from pilots is an area that has not had enough attention, is an extremely complex area and would benefit from further work.

Of particular importance is meeting the challenge for those that have proven success, of launching them widely and making them more generally available – a more expensive exercise than the development of prototypes. There will be harder political decisions to be made about priorities and the level of children's well-being that the country is prepared to pay for.

There is a need to ensure that these initiatives are integrated into the existing mechanisms for planning and for setting priorities, such as Children's Services Plans, early years development plans, education development plans, behaviour support plans, work on primary care groups, etc. There should not be any duplication of effort in attracting the new funding opportunities.

HARMONISING LEGISLATION AND GUIDANCE

Reviewing Manchester's initiative *Championing Children*, which achieved considerable success bringing together education and social services provision for young children, Richard Leese[3] outlined changes by government that would facilitate such developments.

- Ensuring all legislation affecting children is compatible, eg Local Authority Social Services Act 1970 and housing legislation (also the 1981 Education Act which engaged educational psychologists in the statementing process, which effectively resulted in their withdrawal from child and adolescent mental health services).
- A duty placed on health authorities to work with local authorities to develop integrated services for children.
- Harmonisation of education, social services and health assessment and intervention guidance relating to troubled children. An example of helpful moves looks to be the proposed harmonisation of draft guidance from Department for Education and Employment and Department of Health on child care inspection and regulation and shifting responsibility for Section 19 day care reviews under the Children Act from social services to education.

The Children Act

The Children Act and related guidance, and that on Children's Services Plans, looks promising as a vehicle for delivering effective child and adolescent mental health services, but in ensuring the local education and health authorities' contribution, there are qualifying clauses within Section 27 relating to resources which go some way to explaining the lack of a cohesive service.

The National Priorities Guidance for Health and Social Care, issued in September 1998 jointly to the National Health Service and Social Services Authorities, has specific reference to the need for a range of advice, consultation and care within primary care and local authority settings, as well as the development of coherent child and adolescent mental health services. The promise of £84 million over three years, divided between the Health Service Modernisation Fund and the Mental Health Grant for local authorities, set aside to improve child and adolescent mental health services, is a welcome first step. The challenge is to ensure that those areas most in need of services are able to attract the necessary resources, particularly in relation to personnel, develop new cultures and mechanisms for effective multiagency working, and systems of consultation and accountability with local communities in order to deliver the much needed services at a preventive, early intervention and specialist level. Certainly, the injection of further resources is necessary for this to take place.

Many social services authorities, for example, have been engaged in important 'refocusing' work since 1995. However, for others, a lack of funding has seriously hampered this work. Whilst the new Priorities Guidance will go some way to assisting with this 'refocusing' process, for both social services and health authorities, the range of services and changes that are needed in order to promote children's mental health effectively necessitates a greater focus and priority for this area.

Children's Services Plans

The potential to develop Children's Services Plans, making them the corporate responsibility of local authorities and ensuring the involvement of the National Health Service in drawing up and implementation of plans, is extremely welcome. However, there is little evidence yet of their effectiveness in practice.

In the production of Children's Service Plans, local authorities are to consult with health authorities and trusts, local education authorities, voluntary organisations, the police and the probation service. The plan should apply to any child in need, including children with disabilities, those with mental health problems, 'looked-after' children, young people leaving care, young runaways, young carers and those in conflict with the law. It should cover services for under eights, family support for those in need and child protection.

Some authorities are making the system work – establishing a single, separate budget for some services or having one agency run all mental health services, but in others effective liaison has broken down. Arrangements such as these are threatened when one agency wishes to make cuts and/or when different or new priorities emerge, as in the case of education and social services departments withdrawing educational psychologists and social workers from child and adolescent mental health services in the 80s and early 90s.

A question that the Inquiry has repeatedly considered is whether one agency should take the lead on child mental health or whether multiagency partners can provide effective and dynamic implementation, despite their different financial commitment and agency allegiance.

Such issues must be addressed and workable solutions developed at national and local level. Potential models may be found from new initiatives in other areas, eg those new multiagency structures relating to young offenders, drugs and adult mental health.

STRUCTURES TO PROMOTE THE INTERESTS OF CHILDREN

Many previous inquiries and reports have made recommendations as to how cross-agency initiatives can be sustained and facilitated by central and local government structures.

For example, the Gulbenkian inquiry into effective government structures for children recommended

- incorporation of the United Nations Convention on the Rights of the Child into United Kingdom law

- all legislation affecting children, from education to social security, should be based on common principles established by the United Nations Convention, eg a child's welfare is a primary consideration in all actions concerning them; non-discrimination; a child's view should be given due regard in all matters affecting him/her.

Some alternative structures to achieve this were proposed:
- the need to focus on processes demonstrating political commitment – to be Prime Ministerially led
- Minister of State for children located in the cabinet office
- senior cabinet minister with responsibility for children
- standing interministerial groups on children
- parliamentary select committee for children, with remit to cut across departments whereas other select committees follow departmental specialisation
- an independent commissioner for children's rights
- child impact statements for all legislation
- the use of Children's Services Plans to lead local planning
- departmental structures that facilitate interagency collaboration for children
- parliamentary procedures that facilitate holistic consideration of children's lives and that involve children, parents and those working with children in the development of policy.

The Government has recently announced its own views on developing government structures in relation to children's rights and safeguards in its response to The Utting Report.[4] It has been decided that the Ministerial Task Force on Children's Safeguards should meet periodically to help government monitor the implementation of its response to the review.[5] It has been argued that while this task force continues, there is no need to create further cross-departmental machinery in this area. However, children's mental health has been so neglected, that the time is ripe to focus special attention on this area.

CHALLENGES FOR THE FUTURE

There will be major challenges involved in a programme which is engaged as much with attitudinal changes, on the part of the public and professionals, as it is with developing existing and new services.

For example, the skilling up and resourcing of mainstream services to deliver help and support to children and young people experiencing a wide range of mental health problems will be as much a matter of professional will as of physical and financial resources. We are aware that there are those currently working within the field who believe that such a broad approach to children's mental health is misplaced, and that child and adolescent mental health services should be concerned only with those children with more severe and enduring problems, with any extension of this resulting in the overmedicalisation of what they see as intrinsically social and emotional problems. Such critics of a more holistic approach argue that increasing the ability of mainstream agencies to assess and intervene with children and young people experiencing mental health problems will only lead to increasing numbers of them accessing specialist services.

However, the experience of one of the few evaluated community mental health services[6] clearly shows that this is not the case. Whilst the community-based services themselves were able to access more children and young people, this was not reflected in an increase in referrals to tier three services (see Appendices Six and Seven for descriptions of the service tiers). The experience of the specialist services submitting evidence to the Inquiry also suggests that the majority of child and adolescent mental health services are currently overwhelmed with increasing numbers of children and young people, many of whom they believed could have been worked with earlier within mainstream services. There are also the moral arguments, described in Chapter One – we know that the majority of children experiencing mental health problems do not access specialist services, and that many of them and their families often struggle on for years without access to help and support (parents' evidence). We also know that early interventions are effective, both in relation to long-term outcomes for children and cost-effectiveness.

The challenges in the arena of children and young people's mental health are more complex than in many other areas. However, in the current more favourable political climate, with positive changes in all aspects of policy-making in relation to children being introduced, we are optimistic that change can begin. This will require though the commitment of all concerned, from the Government down to local communities.

The range of challenges which are confronting the nation include such diverse areas as the following.

Changing public attitudes towards both children and mental health

The Government has recognised the importance of work to reduce stigma associated with mental ill health in relation to young people through its recent work with the HEA. The importance of such projects, targeted at children, young people, parents and the general public cannot be underestimated. We believe the challenge for all agencies potentially involved in such work, from the Government through to agencies like the Mental Health Foundation, is ensuring that such programmes of 'public education' are both relevant, effective and effectively evaluated.

Developing partnerships

The development of effective partnerships between specialist mental health, primary care and community-based professionals, and between professionals, parents and young people, also presents great challenges. Changing professionals' attitudes has implications for their initial and post-qualifying training and the location of their services. Commissioners and service providers will need to develop the involvement of parents and children in designing services. Increasing the information available to children, young people, parents and families and their ability to access services will require imagination and the involvement of community and specialist agencies.

Developing new ways of delivering services

One of the greatest challenges must lie in developing services which are accessible, especially for those who are the most vulnerable. Those who are in most need are very often those who are the least likely to access services – the 'inverse care law'. Models of community empowerment, of effective ways of consultation and involvement, and of developing and delivering services which are responsive to the real needs of clients must be developed. We believe it is of the utmost priority to further develop and evaluate those models of innovative work in this area.

Meeting the needs of minority ethnic groups

Currently, issues of race and culture are overlooked in the development and provision of services for children and young people experiencing mental health problems. It is vital that this omission is addressed. We are not so naive as to suggest that such a task will be straightforward; encompassing as it must the development within all professions working with children, young people and their families a real sensitivity to the cultural beliefs and practices of those they are working with, the necessary changes in professional practice such approaches will necessitate, and the development of resources – both in relation to professionals, appropriate research and information to support this.

One of the main priority areas for further work for the Foundation itself is to develop the body of knowledge in relation to race, culture and children's mental health in order to facilitate this process. In addition to this, we believe that it is vital that all services working with children and young people must address issues of race and culture in all aspects of their practice. This is particularly important for those services that exist in areas with high minority ethnic populations. It is vital that these services
- have access to support in order to facilitate their work with minority ethnic families, children and young people, ie easy access to interpretive services
- are especially sensitive to meeting the needs of the local population.

Whilst we would recommend the necessity of staff teams which reflect the diversities of the local population, it is important that this is not at the expense of an increased understanding of and sensitivity to the needs of different cultural and ethnic groups on the part of all staff. This will require training for all those professionals working in this area.

OUR OVERARCHING CONCLUSIONS

**The mental health of children and
young people is everyone's business**

Adult society as a whole needs to recognise the importance of children's mental health and emotional literacy and the responsibility everyone has for the 'mental' dimensions of all our lives, specifically:
- government needs to take responsibility for ensuring that the mental health dimension of children's lives is reflected in all its programmes and spending priorities
- the media has an important role to play in creating a climate in which such issues can be more easily talked about and better understood, and in making information more widely available
- professionals have a responsibility not only to their individual patients, clients or students, but also to their communities and to society as a whole
- citizens have a responsibility not only for themselves and their immediate families or households, but also for their fellow citizens who may be excluded, vulnerable or distressed.

**Investing in children's mental health
is an investment in our futures**

Like academic intelligence and physical health, emotional intelligence and mental health do not just happen, they cost money and need skilled resources.

- Government needs to recognise the value of ensuring such an investment is made, it needs to carry out a detailed analysis of resources that are needed and where they should go, including measuring the long-term cost gains of early promotion and interventions. Such a review must address the enormous regional variations in the level and effectiveness of services.

- Although early action may prevent many children and young people developing more severe problems, there will always be those who need specialist help. Such help should be of the highest quality and easily accessed.

- Government should take immediate action to address the chronic shortage of appropriately skilled professionals in almost every aspect of children's mental health and social care (including those for whom mental health is only a dimension of their work), and should convene a task force with representatives of the appropriate professional and training bodies to develop a 'manpower' development plan.

- Parents and families are the most important players of all. Government should build on its important initiative on the family to ensure that not only is the mental health dimension fully recognised, but that its other policies are consistent with valuing and supporting the family. Family poverty is an important risk factor for developing mental health problems, and government needs to take this into account when looking at its policies on taxation, benefits, etc.

Services need clear frameworks, standards and leadership

- Legislation should establish a statutory duty for local authorities, health authorities, social services authorities and education authorities to cooperate in promoting children's mental health. The legislation should require government to develop a National Service Framework (similar to that being developed for adult mental health services) for children's mental health, with clear targets for health, social services and education authorities, in order that each shall meet their responsibilities.

- Whilst welcoming government strategies to improve interagency working at both national and local government level, and recognising some improvement, we nevertheless feel that there is a need for a permanent group to provide national leadership, ensure that all relevant government initiatives fully take account of the mental health dimension and to advise on standards and service delivery. We recommend that government should now convene a working party to explore the feasibility of establishing a national advisory committee on the emotional and mental health of children (the recently formed Youth Justice Board could be a useful model). Such a committee should also be mirrored at the local level.

RECOMMENDATIONS FOR IMPROVING THE MENTAL HEALTH OF CHILDREN AND YOUNG PEOPLE

	All ages	Pre-birth	0-4 years	5-10 years	11-15 years	16-25 years
Promotion	• Campaigns to raise awareness • Family-friendly working hours • Antipoverty/social inclusion measures	• Universal pre-birth support	• Increased health visitor screening/post-natal support • Universal *Sure Start* type schemes • Universal pre-school provision/education			
			• Social services via Children's Services Plans – network of accessible early intervention schemes • Primary care groups – assessment and early intervention			
				• Holistic school league tables for social and mental well-being, creative and sporting achievement • Whole school peer education, antibullying programmes • Boost PSHE and mental health coordinator • Out-of-school provision in disadvantaged areas • Mentoring and other schemes for black and ethnic minority pupils • Increase school psychological service – for school-based programmes, direct work with children and families • Training for teachers in mental health, behaviour management, child development		
Early intervention	• Universal parent support • Support for families undergoing break-up • Impact analysis on all government policies		• Home visiting for at risk families • In-patient facilities for mentally ill mothers and babies, joint funded		• Expand mainstream youth service • Network of long-term funded, accessible, informal youth projects	
Specialist services	• Interprofessional training • National Service Framework and National Board • Research and dissemination				• Full child and adolescent mental health services for young people in young offender institutions and prisons	• Sensitive transition arrangements for 18-25 year-olds between child and adolescent mental health services and adult services • Appropriate in-patient facilities for under 25s • No under 18s on adult wards
			• Mental health assessment for all children entering care • Named doctor, nurse or formal links with GP for all looked-after children and access to full child and adolescent mental health services • Joint funded four-tier child and adolescent mental health services • Statutory health lead, defined responsibilities for education and social services with ring-fenced funding • Staff recruitment, training and development strategy produced by DoH, RCN, BPS, RCP			

This information constitutes a regrouping of those recommendations which are dispersed throughout the report and which are particularly aimed at government.
For a fuller summary of the recommendations aimed at their particular target audiences see Appendix Eight.

1 *The Big Picture* (1999) Mental Health Foundation, London

2 Rutter, M Giller, H Hagell, A (1998) *Antisocial behaviour by Young People. A Major New Review of the Research* Cambridge University Press.

3 Leese, R (July 1998) *Integrated Local Structures, the view from Manchester Comprehensive Spending Review of Provision for Children* Supporting Papers vol 2, HM Treasury

4 Utting, W (1998) *People Like Us: The Report of the Review of the Safeguards for Children living away from Home* HMSO, London

5 The Government's Response to the Children's Safeguards Review (November 1998) HMSO, London

6 Day, C Davis, H Hind, R (1998) *The development of a community child and family mental health service* Child: Care, Health and Development vol 24 pp487-500

APPENDIX 1

MEMBERSHIP OF THE INQUIRY

Inquiry Chair: **Tessa Baring** CBE, Chair of Policy Coordination Committee, National Lottery Charities Board

Brenda Allen, Former Assistant Director – Childcare, Barnados

Sondra Arning, Psychotherapist

Claire Blackman, The Audit Commission

Helen Dent, Chief Executive, Family Welfare Association

David Faulkner, Fellow of St John's College, Oxford University

Moira Gibb, Director of Social Services, Kensington and Chelsea

Roger Graef, Broadcaster

Dr Alyson Hall, Lead Clinical Manager, Child and Adolescent Mental Health, Tower Hamlets Healthcare NHS Trust

Professor Peter Hill, Professor of Child and Adolescent Psychiatry, Department of Psychological Medicine, The Hospital for Sick Children, Great Ormond Street

David Lake, Education Authority, Birmingham City Council

F A May, Deputy Chief Constable, Dorset Police

Angela Neustatter, Journalist

Dr Anula Nikapota, Child and Adolescent Psychiatrist, Brixton Child Guidance Unit

Barbara Rayment, Director, Youth Access

Dr Nicky Salt, General Practitioner

Dr Stephen Scott, Senior Lecturer, Department of Child and Adolescent Psychiatry, Institute of Psychiatry

Dr Hilary Standing, Institute of Development Studies, University of Sussex

Dr Mary Target, Senior Lecturer, Department of Psychology, University College London

Peter Wilson, Director, Young Minds

In attendance

Cedric Dowe, Department for Education and Employment

Dr Bob Jezzard, Department of Health

Staff members

Helen Kay, Project Manager and Report Writer

Nigel Duerdoth

Lucy Leon

June McKerrow

Paul O'Connell

Cliff Prior

Jacent Tracey

Consultants and advisers

Vida Field

Gordon McKerrow

Ann Richardson

APPENDIX 2

THE INQUIRY PROCESS

This Committee of Inquiry was established by the Mental Health Foundation in March 1997, to look at what is needed for the emotionally and mentally healthy development of children, and the needs of those children who have mental health problems. The Inquiry took a broad perspective, looking at issues of parenting, and the ways in which our social structures help or hinder good parenting, along with the roles of education, juvenile justice and youth work, as well as at health and social services aspects.

The aims of the Inquiry were to
• promote the mental health of children and young people in Britain
• examine what is needed for the emotionally and psychologically healthy development of children
• examine the needs and provision for those children who have mental health problems.

Its objectives were to
• gain an understanding of the wishes and needs of children and young people and those at risk of and experiencing mental health problems
• review services and care for children with mental health problems and make recommendations for their improvement
• identify models of good practice in promoting mentally healthy development and in meeting the needs of those who have mental health problems
• raise children and young people's public, and professional awareness and understanding
• improve the integration of aims, policy and services across the full range of people and agencies involved.

In order to meet these aims, the Inquiry membership was drawn from a wide range of backgrounds, including representatives from the fields of child psychiatry, psychology, social services, juvenile justice, education, general practitioners, voluntary sector agencies, the media.

The process

The Inquiry met every two months to consider both written and oral evidence. The breadth of evidence and the rigor of the membership have been central to its success, giving a broad-based authoritative legitimacy to the findings and recommendations within this report.

The range of inputs to the Inquiry have included
• eight main Inquiry meetings
• evidence subgroups on specific areas of interest
• calls for evidence aimed at children, young people, parents and professionals
• focus groups with parents and young people
• weekend workshops with young people who had experienced mental health problems
• specifically commissioned research for the Inquiry.

APPENDIX 3

EVIDENCE TO THE INQUIRY

The Committee received more than 1,000 submissions of evidence.

Professionals

208 submissions of written evidence were received from professionals.

Parents

We received 204 submissions of written evidence from parents of children with mental health problems. Parents participating in the Inquiry in this way were targeted primarily through their contact with mental health services, voluntary mental health organisations and support networks involved with carers for children with such problems as attachment disorder, attention deficit hyperactivity disorder, schizophrenia and eating disorders. A qualitative analysis was carried out – the results of which was produced into a supporting report.[1]

A Search Conference involving parents and professionals was held. Parents were recruited for this through parents organisations and mental health services. In addition to this, two focus groups were held with parents, one in Manchester and one in Cardiff. Parents were recruited to these through parent organisations, and through the network of those parents unable to attend the Search Conference. The discussions from these were written up and presented to the Inquiry group.

Children and young people

We received 400 submissions from children under 10, and 180 submissions from children over 10. The children under 10 participating in this way were targeted primarily through Special Educational Needs coordinators in a number of education authorities, and through the primary schools funded under the Mental Health Foundation's *Bright Futures* initiative. Those over 10 were contacted principally through the Mental Health Foundation's website, youth agencies and secondary schools. Qualitative analysis of this evidence was carried out, the results of which are available from the Mental Health Foundation.

Six focus groups were held with young people. The main focus for these groups was to
- reach young people with a wide range of experiences of mental health difficulties
- gather information on what young people think and feel about professionals and the services they have been in contact with
- gather information on their experiences with parents/carers, extended family and peers in relation to the difficulties they encountered.

Three out of the six groups were held in hospitals where young people were either in-patients or attending an out-patients group therapy session, and the other three in community youth projects. Each focus group addressed a particular issue. These were the care system, eating disorders, self-harm, and two groups focused on the experiences of young people from minority ethnic backgrounds. An analysis of the groups is available from the Mental Health Foundation.

Weekend workshops

Two weekends were held with groups of young people in order to gain their views. Young people were recruited for these weekends from a large number of voluntary projects working with vulnerable young people. The experiences and views of young people attending the weekends were written up into a discussion document, and presented to the Inquiry group. In addition to this, young people from the weekends were invited to make oral presentations to the main Inquiry meetings.

A series of papers was specifically commissioned for the Inquiry on
- the broader social context of children's lives (The Family Policy Studies Centre)
- mapping the existence of parenting support programmes in various areas (Parenting and Education Support Forum)
- a study into the factors associated with high and low self-esteem in boys and girls (Adrienne Katz and Dr Buchannan from Oxford University)
- the role of cost benefit analysis in assessing spending programmes aimed at improving the mental health and general well-being of children and adolescents (Sally Holterman).

In addition to this, the Inquiry drew upon results from the Mental Health Foundation's three-year programme on child and adolescent mental health. This included results from
- community-based projects focused on developing young people's voices in relation to mental health services
- a programme to develop whole school approaches to promote the mental health of four to seven year-olds
- the funding of community-based projects working with depressed mothers and their children
- an 18-month social research project into how children and young people conceptualise mental health
- a programme of biomedical research into child and adolescent mental health.

Organisations and professionals giving evidence

The Mental Health Foundation would like to thank everyone who took part in this Inquiry, especially those who submitted written and oral evidence. We would particularly like to thank those parents and young people who took the time to take part in the events organised around the Inquiry – the Search Conference, Focus Groups and the Young People's weekends.

We do not feel that it would be appropriate to include the names of all those individuals who took part in the focus groups or the weekends, but we would like mention those young people's organisations who were particularly supportive in helping us to set up and run these.

Young people organisations

42nd Street, Manchester; Sandwell Community Health Council; Bypass, Bolton; Brunswick Project, Newcastle; Lifechance Project, Oxford; Young People, Cornwall; The Base, Whitley Bay; Youth Enquiry Service, Plymouth.

We would also like to thank all those parent organisations and support groups who distributed questionnaires and showed interest in the Inquiry. These are too numerous to mention.

Names of those giving oral evidence

Claire Armstrong, University of Glasgow
Colin Bell, young person from 42nd Street, Manchester
Dorothy Brown, Exploring Parenthood
Professor Helen Cowie, Roehampton Institute
Alistair Cox, 42nd Street, Manchester
Jo Curling, young person from Hear Our Voice – Young People, Cornwall
Ian Davies, young person from 42nd Street, Manchester

Dr Jessie Earle, St George's Hospital
Geoffrey Evans, C'mon Everybody, Sheffield
Dr Chris Everitt, Wirral Health Authority
John Flynn, Primary Mental Health Worker, Dorset
Simone Francis, Young person from Lifechance, Oxford
Caroline Gibbs, Young person from Lifechance, Oxford
Dr Vivette Glover, Institute of Obstetrics and Gynaecology, Department
of Paediatrics, Queen Charlotte and Chelsea Hospital
Mark Gringrod, The Howard League
John Hawkins, East Sussex Social Services Department
Dr Anne Hayden, General Practitioner, Dorset
Ruth Hudson, Community Practitioners and Health Visitors Association
Dame Tamsyn Imison, Headteacher, Hampstead School
Gabriel Jones, Pre-school Learning Alliance
Dr Tony Kaplan, SAFE, Services for Adolescents and Families in Enfield
John Leach, Department of Health
Dr Michael Little, Dartington Social Research Centre
Dinah Morley, Young Minds
Jane Mountenay, Institute for the Study of Drug Dependency
Andy Murphy, young person from 42nd Street, Manchester
Julie Murray, young person from 42nd Street, Manchester
Professor Lynne Murray, Department of Psychology, University of Reading
Dr Mel Parr, Pippin
Nick Peacey, SENJIT, Institute of Education
Sue Pettigrew, St Michael's Fellowship, London
Toni Selby, young person from Hear Our Voice – Young People, Cornwall
Professor Ian Sinclair, University of York
Roger Smith, Children's Society
Professor Mike Stein, University of York
Jenny Vernon, National Children's Bureau

Organisations and professionals giving written evidence to the Inquiry

Organisations

42nd Street, Manchester
Aberdeen Children's Society
The Base, Whitley Bay
Barnardos Rhondda Family Centre
Barnardos West Lothian Family Support Team, Bathgate
Birch Hill Hospital Child & Adolescent Unit, Rochdale
Bishop Harvey Family Service, Hendon
British Medical Association, London
Brynffynnon Child and Family Service, Pontypridd
Cambridgeshire City Council Education Department, Secondary Learning
    Support Centre, Peterborough
Canadian Mental Health Association
Centre 33, Cambridge
Centrepoint, Soho, London
Child and Adolescent Clinical Psychology Service, University Hospital of Wales
Child and Family Consultation Service, Swindon
Cheshire Family & Child Advisory Service
Community Education Youth Advice Careline, Youth Advice Centre, Ipswich
Community Section, Riverside Mental Health Trust Child Psychology Service,
    Community Child Joint Croydon Youth Development Unit

East Wiltshire Healthcare Trust, Wroughton
Elms Health Centre, Cradley, West Midlands
English Sport Council, London
Family and Child Advisory Service, Warrington
Family and Residential Placement and Fieldwork Services, Norwood House, Hendon
Haringey Educational Psychology Service, London
Hertfordshire Constabulary, Welwyn Garden City
Integrated Support Service, London Borough of Merton
Kent County Council, Medway and Swale Area, Sittingbourne
Kings Cross Community Development Project, London
LARCH – The Children's Society, Leeds
Liverpool Children's Project
Loddon NHS Trust, Child and Family Services
London Borough of Islington, Neighbourhood Services Head Office
MOLE Scarborough/Whitby, Ryedale User & Carer Involvement Project
National Stepfamily Association
National Youth Agency
No Limits, Information, Advice and Counselling Service, Southampton
Norfolk Psychological Service, Norwich
Northumbria Police, Crime Management and Community Safety, Police HQ
    Newcastle-upon-Tyne
Off The Record, Bath
Off The Record Youth Counselling, Croydon
Outreach Support Service, Eastleigh, Hants
Onslow St Audrey's School
Pact Project, NCH Action for Children, Perth
Parentline UK, Hadleigh, Essex
Parent Network, London
Planning Officer, Leicestershire Joint Strategy Group, Leicestershire Health Authority
Rochdale Social Services Child and Adolescent Team
SHINE Project, The Children's Society, London
Stillborn and Neonatal Death Society (SANDS), London
The Arts Connection – Cumberland Centre, Portsmouth
The Bloomfield Clinic, Guy's and St Thomas' Hospital, London
The Church of Scotland Social Work, Geisland School, Beth, Ayrshire
The Collies, NCH Action For Children, Coleford, Gloucestershire
The Highfield Family and Adolescent Unit, The Warneford Hospital, Oxford
The Integrated Support Service, London Borough of Merton
The Ridgewood Centre, West Surrey Health Authority
The Royal College of Psychiatrists
Thomas Coram Foundation for Children, London
Whitsone Head Educational Trust, Whitsone Head School, Devon
Witney Child and Family Clinic, Witney, Oxfordshire
Youth Access
Youth and Families Matter, Totton
Youth Enquiry Service, Kendal

Professionals
Ameena Ahmed, Off the Record, Young People's Centre, Manchester
Anna Amin, East Midlands Arts Board
Norma Angeli, Redwoods, Surrey
Pamela Apperley, Health Visitor, Alton Street Surgery
Eleanor Armitage, National Pyramid Trust, Bristol
Marlene Arthur, Linn Moore Residential School, Aberdeen
Anne Ashby, Rotherham Social Services

Dr Louise Atkin, Winnicott Centre, Manchester

Sue Bailey, School of Social Work, University of East Anglia

Sue Baker, Alcohol Concern, London

Keith Baldwin, Superintendent, Hertfordshire Constabulary

Dr Jacqueline Barnes, Leopold Muller University Department of Child and Family Mental Health, Royal Free Hospital School of Medicine, London

Gerard Barrie, Dimensions Art Studio

Joanne Barton, Department of Adolescent and Child Psychiatry, University of Glasgow

Carol Bates, Royal College of Midwives, London

Celia M Beckett, British Agencies for Adoption and Fostering, London

Helen Beinart, Special Interest Group (Children and Young People), British Psychological Society

Patrick Belas, Andover Family Clinic

Marion Bennathan, The Association of Workers for Children with Emotional and Behavioural Disabilities, Baldock

Dr Caroline Blair, Consultant Clinical Psychologist, Young People's Unit, Edinburgh

Lynne Bold, Star Children's Centre, St Helens

Stephen Boyce, Southern Arts Board

Greg Boys, Assistant Divisional Officer, Royal Berkshire Fire & Rescue Service

Anna Brazier, Rhondda NHS Trust Clinical Psychology Department, Pontypridd

Dr Bob Broad, Department of Social and Community Studies, De Montfort University, Leicester

Dr Julian Brockless, Slough Family & Child Guidance Service

Gwyneth Bruce, Young People's Unit, Edinburgh

Jane Bryant, Southern Arts Board

Chris Burton, Prinicipal Officer (Quality Assurance), Suffolk Social Services

Sheryl Burton, National Children's Bureau, London

Maria Camenzul, Nurses Residence, Fulbourne

D Cash, Child Protection Unit, Dorset Police

M F Cassidy, Low Newton Remand Centre, Brosside, Durham

Elizabeth Chekanoff, Policy Officer – Families & Young People, Dorset County Council, Social Services Directorate

Sandra Chilton, University of Northumbria Student Services

Elisabeth Clarke, Swale Mental Health Team, Kent

P J Clarke, Inspector, West Mercia Constabulary

Anne Claveirole, Faculty of Health Studies, Napier University

Sally Collings, Off The Record, Wansdyke

C Cook, Associate Dean and Head of Department of Education, University of Hertfordshire

Professor Helen Cowie, Roehampton Institute

Professor John L Cox, School of Postgraduate Medicine, Keele University

Julie Cox, Coordination and Development Officer, North Thames Community Health Council

Professor Illana B Crome, Professor of Addiction Studies, University of Wolverhampton, School of Health Sciences

N Davies, Youth Justice Officer, Dorset Police

Dr Nadia Davis, Institute of Psychiatry, London

Carolyn Douglas, Exploring Parenthood, London

Phil Doyle, Project Manager, (RPS/Rainer) Mid-Surrey Stepping out Project

Madeline Drake, Richmond Fellowship

Rosemary Drewett, Spurgeon's Family Centre

Dr Chris Drinkwater, Department of Primary Care, University of Newcastle

Alan Dyson, Special Needs Research Centre, University of Newcastle

Dr Naomi Elton, Consultant Psychiatrist, North Essex Child and Family Consultation Service

Hazel Endersby, Queensway Teachers Centre, Milton Keynes

Gill Evans, Special Education Support & Psychology Services, North Somerset Council

Gerald Finnegan, Mind Yourself Mental Health Charity, Co Derry

S M Finney, Bull Plain Health Centre, Hertford

Paul F J Flemming, Lecturer in Clinical Psychology, University of Glasgow

Dr D Forster, Consultant Psychiatrist, Treliske Hospital, Truro

Dr Ian Frampton, Maudsley Hospital, London

Joseph P Gavan, Senior Charge Nurse, HMP Hockley

Dave Gibbs, Hertfordshire County Council

M Gibson, Services Development Manager, South Cheshire Health Authority

M J Gibson, South Cheshire Health Authority

Kathryn Gifoy, Studio 3 Arts

Dr Vivette Glover, Institute of Obstetrics and Gynaecology, Department of Paediatrics, Queen Charlotte and Chelsea Hospital

Dr Michael Goepfert, Consultant Psychotherapist, Liverpool Psychotherapy and Consultation Service, Mossley Hill Hospital

Dr Robert Goodman, Institute of Psychiatry

Sue Goulding, Clinical Psychologist, Rosemead Centre, Doncaster

M Graham, Atkinson Unit, Devon Social Services

Gay Gray, University of Southampton

Dawn Gregory, Norfolk Social Services Department

Dr Alyson Hall, Emmanuel Miller, Royal London Hospital and Tower Hamlets Child and Adolescent Mental Health Service

Christine Hancock, Royal College of Nursing, London

David Hands, Independence Support Project, Isle of Wight Social Services Department

Professor Richard Harrington, Professor of Child & Adolescent Psychiatry, Royal Manchester Children's Hospital

Margaret Harrison, Home-Start UK, Leicester

Stephen Harwood, Principal Policy and Practice Officer, Barnardos

Gary Hayes, Institute for the Study of Drug Dependency, London

Christine Hayward, Child and Adolescent Directorate, Colchester

Dr Kevin Healy, Adolescent Unit, Cassel Hospital, Richmond

Alison Heard, City General Hospital, Department of Clinical Psychology, Stoke on Trent

Barbara Herts, National Children's Bureau, London

Joy Higginson, Children North East

Lynne Hipkin, Acting Principal Officer, Community Section, Riverside Mental Health Trust, Child Psychology Service

G Hiscox, Lancashire LEA

Rachel Hodgkin, Principal Policy Officer, National Children's Bureau

Elizabeth Mary Hume, Specialist Health Visitor, Leeds Community and Mental Health Trust

Dr Judy Hutchings, Bangor Project for Children with Disruptive Behaviours, School of Psychology, University of Wales

Daphne Jones, Outreach Liaison Teacher, Croydon

Ella Jones, Health Promotion Service Manager, North Glamorgan NHS Trust, Mountain Ash General Hospital

Megan Jones, Research and Development Manager, APA Community Drug and Alcohol Initiatives, London

Gabrielle Jones, Special Needs Coordinator, Preschool Learning Alliance, London Regional Office

Tony Kaplan, Consultant Adolescent Psychiatrist, Enfield Community Care NHS Trust

Frances Keen, Policy Officer, National Lottery Charities Board

Ruth Kennedy, Huyton Community Development Project, The Children's Society

Kate Kennet, Art Therapist & Project Coordinator, Mental Health Services, Salford

Professor Michael Kerfoot, Child and Adolescent Policy and Research, School of Psychiatry and Behavioural Sciences, University of Manchester

Dr Geoffrey D Kewley, Learning Assessment Centre, Horsham

Jill Kidger, Child and Family Consultation Service, Vale Drive Clinic, London

Dr David Kinnard, Bethel Child and Family Centre, Norwich

Karen Kirkman, Regional Arts Board, West Midlands

Peter Kohn, Business Manager, Children's Services, West Herts Community NHS Trust

Madeleine Knowles, Child & Family Consultation Service, Newham

Dr Sebastian Kraemer, Child & Adolescent Psychiatrist, Tavistock Clinic, London

Dr Simon Lalonde, Child Psychology Services, City Hospital, Birmingham

Peter W Lane, Southern Area Education Office, County Hall, Ipswich

John Leach, Department of Health

J L Leishman, Head of Nursing, University of Abertay, Dundee

Sarah Leslie, Young People's Unit, Edinburgh

Dr Stuart Lieberman, Ridgewood Centre, Camberley

Rosemary Lilley, Newbury Family Counselling Service, NCH Action for Children

Dr Stephen Littlewood, Department of Child Psychiatry, Countess of Chester Hospital NHS Trust

Jane Livingstone, Alcohol Advisory and Counselling Service, Aberdeen

Eva Lloyd, Principal Officer Research and Development, Barnardos, Essex

Judith Green Loose, Vale Drive Child Guidance Clinic, London

Lindsey Lovatt, Longview Unit, Colchester

John Lucy, Manchester Health Authority

Anne Mason, Childline, London

Karen Macleod, Senior Probation Officer, Brockhill Women's Prison

Liz Malcom, Division of Educational and Child Psychology, British Psychological Society

Dr Natasha Mauthner, Research Unit in Health and Behavioural Change, University of Edinburgh

Cathy Maxwell, Voluntary Service, Aberdeen

Catherine McCarthy, Camden and Islington Health Authority

Professor James McEwen, Department of Public Health, University of Glasgow

Anne McFadyen, Tavistock Clinic, London

Marilyn McGowan, British Association of Counselling

Derek McLean, Barnardos 16+ Project, Edinburgh

Nick McMullen, Leicestershire County Council

Dr Fiona McNicholas, Guys Hospital

P Mayes, Child and Family Consultation Service, Princess Margaret Hospital

Philip Messent, Social Work Team Manager, London Borough of Tower Hamlets

Dr Janet Moore, Brixton Child Guidance Unit

Professor Lynne Murray, Department of Psychology, University of Reading

Dr R Nazraj, Brookside Clinic, Aylesbury

Dr Colin Newman, British Psychological Society, London

Lynda M Nolan, Project Leader, Barnardos Chorley Family Project

Dr M R Oates, Department of Psychiatry, University of Nottingham

Margaret Ogden, Haverstock School

Steve Page, Head of Counselling, The University of Hull Counselling Service

Louise Pankhurst, Child Psychotherapy Trust, London

Dr Mel Parr, Pippin

Barbara Parnell, Manic Depression Fellowship Wales, Newport

Dr Carl Parsons, Canterbury Christ Church College, Kent

Fiona Peacock, Student Counsellor, The Luton Sixth Form College

Mary Penwarden, Lenworth Clinic, Ashford

Pat Petterson, May Lodge Family Resource Centre, Scarborough NCH Action
for Children

Sue Pettigrew, St Michael's Fellowship, London

Steven Phillips, Educational Psychologist, Gorgeston on Sea

Dr David Pilgrim, Department of Clinical Psychology, Queens Park Hospital

Dorothy Eddie Piper, Trust for the Study of Adolescence, Brighton

Angela Plowman, Home Start UK

Dr R G Poole, Clinical Director, Acute Directorate, Broadoak Unit, Liverpool

Dr K Puvanendran, St George's Hospital, Essex

Michael Quinn, Family Caring Trust, County Down

Dr T Rangarajan, North Glamorgan NHS Trust

Patrick Robbitt, Age and Cognitive Research Centre, Manchester

Maggie Robinson, Community Education Development Centre, Woodway Park
School, Coventry

Dr G Rose, Child & Adolescent Psychiatrist, North Herts NHS Trust

John Ryland, C'mon Everybody Project, Sheffield

Ray Seabrook, Dingley Centre, Islington Social Services

Rev Dr Peter Sedgwick, Board for Social Responsibility, General Synod,
Church of England

Carol Sexty, National Foster Care Association, London

Gwen Sharpe, Bury & Rochdale Health Authority

Professor M Shearer, School of Health and Nursing, University of
Abertay, Dundee

Professor J R Sibert, Department of Child Health, University of Wales

Dr Fiona Sim, Enfield & Haringey Health Authority

Dr Sheila Simpson, Department of Medical Genetics, University of Aberdeen

Geraldine Shipton, Centre for Psychotherapeutic Studies, The University
of Sheffield

Dr R M Sims, Child and Adolescent Psychiatrist, Wakefield and Pontefract
Community Health Trust

Professor Ian Sinclair, Department of Health Research, University of York

Alison Smith, Survivors' Poetry

Antony P Smith, English National Board for Nursing, Midwifery and Health
Visiting, London

Roger Smith, Social Policy Manager, The Children's Society

Dr Quentin Spender, Child and Family Service for Mental Health, Chichester

Malcolm Stammers, Child and Adolescent Mental Health Service, Bangor

Professor Alan Stein, Royal Free Hospital and the Tavistock Clinic

Dr Eddy Street, Llandough Hospital Children's Centre, Penarth

Carol Sutton, School of Health and Community Studies, Leicester

Dr Mark Tattersag, Huntecombe Manor Hospital, Taplow, Berkshire

Alexis Tayor, Devon County Council Child Protection Unit

Professor Eric Taylor, Institute of Psychiatry, London

James Thatcher, Community Services Division, Norfolk County
Council Education

J Thewlis, Institute of Education

Judy Thompson, (School Nurse) Leominster Community Hospital

Steve Thwaites, Clinical Nurse Manager, Oxfordshire Mental Healthcare,
Highfield Family and Adolescent Unit, The Warneford Hospital

Janice Toulson, Depression Alliance, London

Dr Gillian Turner, Consultant Community Paediatrician, Northumberland Child Health Centre

Dr Peter Turnpenny, Clinical Genetics, Royal Devon & Exeter Hospital

Dr D Vazsier, Treliske Hospital, Truro

Professor Panos Vostanis, Senior Lecturer in Child and Adolescent Psychiatry, University of Birmingham

D A Wakenshaw, Northumbria Police (Crime Management Head Quarters), Newcastle-upon-Tyne

A J Walker, HM Prison Service, Low Newton, Durham

Ian Warwick, Policy Studies Group, Health and Education Research Unit Institute of Education

S Webb, Counselling and Stress Management Professional, Fornby

Jeni Webster, Department of Social Work, Manchester University

Hazel Welch, Signpost, Watford

Dr L Wiggs, Park Hospital for Children, Oxford

Dr A Wigley, Eglywsbach Surgery, Pontypridd

Dr Ian Wilkinson, St Luke's Hospital, Middlesborough

Colleen Williams, The Ridgewood Centre, Camberley

Ian Williams, Child Mental Health Service – The Linhope Unit, Northumberland

Dr Richard Williams, Cornwall Child and Family Services

Jenny Willmot, MIND, London

Dr Alison Wood, Duchess of York Children's Hospital, Manchester

Dr R M Wrate, Consultant Adolescent Psychiatrist, The Young People's Unit, Royal Edinburgh Hospital

Jane Wreford, Special Educational Support and Psychology Services, North Somerset Council

---

1 O'Connell, P (1999) *Parents' evidence to the Inquiry* Mental Health Foundation, London (in press)

APPENDIX 4

SUMMARY OF EFFECTIVE TREATMENTS FOR CHILDREN AND YOUNG PEOPLE EXPERIENCING MENTAL HEALTH PROBLEMS

We have summarised findings relating to a number of mental health problems encountered in children and young people.

What we know works – Effective treatments for children and young people experiencing mental health problems

Conduct/antisocial disorders

We know from research that interventions targeting key risk and resilience factors can be effective. Programmes combining family support with early education have prevented delinquency through their impact on multiple risk factors.

There has been a strong emphasis in recent years on interventions designed to improve the parenting skills of children with behaviour problems. Such work is consistent with research that "family functioning rather than family structure has the greatest impact upon outcomes for children". In Barlow's systematic review of parenting programmes working in this field, the findings were largely positive, showing that group-based parenting programmes did have an impact on improving the behaviour of young children.

The work of Webster-Stratton in the USA shows that for children with clinically defined behaviour problems from high risk backgrounds, videotape modelling can be effective in changing children's behaviour. Parenting courses are a useful tool within a broad range of potential supports for families, particularly where accurate assessments have been made by the parents themselves or others of the need for information or skills training. But if parenting courses are used as stand-alone interventions they are unlikely to have long-lasting effects. Families with long-standing and complex problems are likely to require complex packages of long-term support. A range of work showing particular promise is that in which parent education is carried out alongside interventions with the child in school.

Attention deficit and hyperactivity

These syndromes are characterised by frequent comorbidity and psychosocial adversity. There is a convincing body of research to suggest that psychostimulant medication can produce immediate short-term benefits, as perceived by parents, teachers and others. However, psychostimulant medication is not a cure; its main therapeutic effect is to facilitate parenting and teaching through psychological, educational and social support.

Emotional disorders (or internalising disorders)

These constitute just under half of psychological disturbance in childhood. The treatment of generalised anxiety in children has not been evaluated using behavioural or cognitive methods until recently. However, promising results have been shown by studies of cognitive-behaviour therapy (CBT) with children diagnosed as suffering from over-anxious disorder, despite the possibility of bias due to expectations inherent in a number of the studies.[1]

Behavioural treatments for circumscribed anxiety symptoms, such as phobias, are likely to be effective in younger children.

A recent review of six randomised control trials of eight to 19 year-olds with depression concluded that cognitive-behaviour therapy was of significant benefit, although most participants had moderate depression. Further studies of children experiencing severe depression are needed.

There is little evidence available on the psychodynamic treatment of depression in this age group, although, there are suggestions from retrospective data that the majority of depressed children treated show clinically significant improvement, provided they receive frequent sessions.[2]

Obsessive compulsive disorder (OCD)

This can be successfully treated by behavioural or cognitive behavioural techniques, although combinations of treatments may be required, and relapse is relatively likely. Research has shown that treatment of OCD requires an intensive effort – it is vital to involve parents, teachers and any other carers so that therapy is consistent. It is also important to engage the motivation of the child by careful tailoring of techniques to their appropriate development level.[3]

Post-traumatic stress disorder

There is now a reasonable amount of evidence on post-traumatic stress disorder responding to exposure therapy within a supportive environment.

Anorexia nervosa and bulimia nervosa

Anorexia is a life threatening condition. A variety of treatment approaches are available and should include family and individual psychotherapy, behavioural treatments, availability of in-patient treatment or occasionally medication. The efficacy of family therapy in treating children and young people with anorexia nervosa has been established.[4] The major findings of this study were that family therapy was effective at preventing relapse for patients with an early onset, but that individual therapy was superior for older adults. One of the most important factors in efficacy for young people is their motivation or readiness to change,[5] which may be a more important predictor of outcome than the particular treatment modality.

Sexual abuse

Child sexual abuse has been described as one of the major mental health problems of the last decade. Apart from the immediate impact of abuse on the child, there is also concern that child sexual abuse may be associated with persistent psychological problems, and hence with a range of psychiatric disorders in adults. A review of the research literature[6] concluded that child sexual abuse had long-term implications for mental health, including
- psychological symptoms, guilt, low self-esteem, sleep disturbance
- problem behaviours such as self-harm and drug abuse
- relationship and sexual problems
- psychiatric disorders, particularly depression, anxiety, eating disorders and post-traumatic stress disorder.

A study[7] of the effectiveness of individual psychotherapy and group therapy offered to children who have experienced sexual abuse shows very promising results. After a year of individual or group psychotherapy, the majority of girls who had experienced child sexual abuse showed a significant reduction in psychiatric symptoms and post-traumatic stress disorder. However, about a quarter of them still had some psychological problems which would require further support, and further research is needed to find better ways of predicting who will need this extra help.

Schizophrenia

There is as yet little evidence on the treatment and outcome for children and young people diagnosed as having schizophrenia. In relation to treatment for young adults, pharmacotherapy is a major component of treatment and there is substantial evidence that it is very helpful, particularly the newer, 'atypical' antipsychotic drugs, eg Clozapine, Riserpidone. Work with the child's family may be important for prevention of relapse. Some psychologically-based approaches to management and treatment in young adults appear to have value, eg the work on establishing early interventions by identifying early signs (prodromes) of relapse, but their efficacy with young people still requires much stronger support from adequate research. Thus, there is little basis for generalising to younger age groups. Current research being carried out by Frangou and Wykes is evaluating the use of cognitive remediation techniques with children and young people aged 12 to 19 years, following the successful piloting of this approach in Australia.[8] Young people with schizophrenia may be more responsive to cognitive remediation than older adults with a longer history of illness. If successful, rehabilitative treatments of this kind may complement existing medical and social treatments.

1 Roth, A and Fonagy, P (1996) *What works for Whom: A critical review of psychotherapy research* Guildford Press, New York

2 as in no 1

3 as in no 1

4 Russell, et al (1987) *An evaluation of family therapy in anorexia nervosa and bulimia nervosa* Archives of General Psychiatry vol 44 pp1047-1056

5 Treasure, J L and Ward, A (1997) *Cognitive Analytical Therapy in the treatment of anorexia nervosa* Clinical Psychology and Psychotherapy vol 4 pp62-71

6 Cotsgrove, A and Kolvin, I (1994) *The long-term impact of child sexual abuse* in Tsiantis, J (ed) *Basic Child Psychiatry* pp85-102 Kastaniotis, Athens

7 Trowell and Kolvin (1999) *Lessons from a psychotherapy outcome study* Clinical Child Psychology and Psychiatry vol 4 no 1 pp79-89

8 Wykes, T (1994) *The prediction of outcome in community care: toxicity for patients with cognitive defects* proceedings of seventh winter workshop on schizophrenia

APPENDIX 5

DEVELOPMENT OF A COMMUNITY CHILD AND FAMILY MENTAL HEALTH SERVICE – LEWISHAM AND GUY'S MENTAL HEALTH TRUST, NHS TRUST, MILL STREET PRACTICE, LONDON

A model of an effective community child and family service has been evaluated.[1] This service, the Community Child and Family Service, was established with funding from the Lambeth, Southwark and Lewisham Health Authority to develop and evaluate local community child mental health services. It is staffed by three full-time and one part-time child mental health specialists, six part-time parent advisers, each of whom works one day a week, a full-time assistant psychologist and a full-time secretary/administrator.

The specific aims of the service are to
• improve access to and utilisation of child mental health care
• improve the identification and management of the broad range of child and family mental health difficulties in the community
• develop community-based health promotion, and prevention programmes.

After carrying out a preliminary needs assessment, which identified the high level of needs within the area, and the broad enthusiasm of primary care professionals for such a service, the Community Child and Family Service has developed a series of specific evaluated projects.

Development of primary health care projects

The Parent Adviser Service
This home-based intervention is carried out by health visitors and community paediatric medical officers specially trained in parenting issues and child behavioural management. Criteria for referral to the project are broad, including any families of preschool children with psychosocial problems. This includes psychosocial problems in the children, emotional problems in the parents, relationship difficulties with the family and the presence of stressors, such as chronic illness or disability.

The aims of the intervention are to
• prevent parents feeling stigmatised or belittled
• empower them to use their own resources effectively to manage difficulties confronting them
• be with them and support them while they do so.

The Parent Adviser's role is to facilitate this process via the development of a respectful relationship with the parents. Initially, families are seen weekly, with the frequency of visits reducing gradually, depending upon the needs identified and the aims negotiated with the parents.

The evaluation of the project clearly revealed its benefits. As Davis said in a study of the findings, these "indicate that health visitors and paediatric CMOs, trained and supervised by child mental health specialists, are able to work successfully with needy parents of preschool children in the context of multi psychosocial problems".[2] Whilst the self-esteem of the mothers, and their levels of depression and stress in the parenting role decreased, the anticipated benefits of improved parental relationships and increased social support were not seen, thus highlighting the continuing need for more extensive, intensive, and/or specialist support for some families.[3]

Primary child mental health care clinics

Since Spring 1996, the Service has been working with six local general practitioner practices. Within each practice, on-site clinics have been set up for children and their families with emotional and behavioural difficulties, run by child mental health specialists. In order to facilitate the development of a partnership approach, in addition to direct clinical work, case discussions, joint assessments and clinical advice are also offered to the practice staff, most commonly general practitioners and health visitors. An evaluation of this service is currently being carried out.

Primary prevention of child mental health problems involving health visitors

The service has recently received funding from the Gatsby Charitable Foundation to evaluate the clinical and cost-effectiveness of an innovative strategy to promote parents' abilities to care for the psychosocial development of their children and to prevent parental and child problems. Trained health visitors conduct promotional interviews before and immediately after all new births, whilst at the same time screening for families at risk of developing child mental health problems. The health visitor then works immediately and intensively with those identified as being in need. It is predicted that the training will enhance health visitors' ability to identify families at risk, improve family function and positively influence the well-being and development of the children.

The development of projects in educational settings

School nurse training programme

The service is also engaged in a number of projects within schools. This project has used the lessons from the Parent Adviser model of work with under fives to run training and supervision for a group of school nurses for school-age children. They have gone on to identify appropriate children and families from their current caseload and to work with them as parent advisers. The nurses receive fortnightly supervision from the project team. The effects of this programme on both the children and the nurses are being evaluated.

Intensive school-based intervention programme

In another project, a clinical psychologist has been working intensively for one day a week in a local primary school. The psychologist has

- carried out direct work with pupils and parents referred by teachers and families themselves
- facilitated small problem-focused groups for pupils on issues, such as anger control
- worked with whole classes on health promotion interventions
- provided regular consultation groups for the teaching staff.

Much of the early phase of the work has been focused on ensuring that the staff accept and understand the project. This has proved to be straightforward in relation to the direct clinical service which has received enthusiastic support from the school. However, establishing the right balance with the curriculum and classroom work has been more difficult. It has not always been easy to integrate the aims of the mental health promotion programme with those of the personal and social education programme being taught in class. Teachers have also sometimes found it difficult to have a psychologist working in their classroom. As a result, there has been a shift from whole class work to specific problem-focused groups.

Consultation programme for day nursery officers

The service has also provided a regular consultation service for day nursery officers. This involves day nursery staff in the area receiving fortnightly consultation from a member of the service. Although the effects of this have yet to be determined from the evaluation, the service has already been invited to develop a programme using the Parent Adviser model to train staff from early years centres more extensively and systematically.

1 Day, C Davis, H and Hind, R 1998, *Child: Care, Health and Development* vol 24 no 6 1998

2 Davis, H Spurr, P Cox, A et al (1997) *A description and evaluation of a community child mental health service* Clinical Child Psychology and Psychiatry vol 2 pp221-238

3 Day, C Davis, H Hind, R (1998) *The development of a community child and family mental health service* Child: Care, Health and Development vol 24 pp487-500

APPENDIX 6

THE 'TIERED' APPROACH

The idea of four tiers of services, recommended by the HAS report and generally accepted by those submitting evidence to the Inquiry, is designed to offer a model to identify the styles and levels of specialism involved in offering a comprehensive and coordinated service for children and young people.

It provides a useful way of conceptualising and planning for the whole range of promotional, preventive, early intervention, and specialist services in relation to children and young people's mental health.

The informal tier

This tier comprises those who are engaged in the lives of children and young people, as parents, carers, relatives, friends and neighbours. They, along with the children and young people themselves, are a vital component of any strategy to promote children and young people's mental health and in the delivery of services.

Tier one – primary or direct contact services

Tier one consists of professionals, such as GPs, generic social workers based in community teams, voluntary sector workers, school staff, police, school medical officers, school nurses, health visitors and others who directly and indirectly influence the mental health of children through their work with them. They are usually the first point of contact between a child or family and the child care or health agencies.

Tier two – interventions by specialist child and adolescent mental health service professionals

This tier consists of work done by specialist child and adolescent mental health professionals when they work individually with children, adolescents and their families. Usually, they will be members of the specialist level (tiers two, three and four) multidisciplinary child and adolescent mental health services, through which their work is coordinated. The work of these specialists may take place at their specialist clinics, or at home, in schools, health centres or social services establishments. Staff within tier two services act as gatekeepers for access to tier three and four provision.

Tier three – interventions offered by teams of specialist child and adolescent mental health service staff

This tier consists of services which are more specialised, often by virtue of the complexity of problems presented to them. In this tier, members of specialist multidisciplinary mental health services work in specific therapeutic teams, bringing coordinated interventions to bear on problems such as eating disorders, traumatic stress or developmental disorders. Alongside assessing and treating children and young people, staff at this level provide a teaching and training resource for levels one and two, and act as gatekeepers for entry to the highly specialised services of tier four.

Tier four – highly specialised interventions and care

This tier provides for highly specific and complex problems which require considerable skills and resources. For example, they include in-patient psychiatric provision for adolescents, secure provision, specialist facilities for those with sensory disabilities, or consultation services for those with severe eating disorders, neuropsychiatric disorders, or rare, chronic or life-threatening paediatric disorders.

Working at this highly specialised level of skill, staff in this tier are well equipped to offer role support to those in tiers one, two and three, where they engage in managing difficult or complex cases that might otherwise have required management at tier four.

APPENDIX 7

A STRATEGIC APPROACH TO COMMISSIONING AND DELIVERING A COMPREHENSIVE CHILD AND ADOLESCENT MENTAL HEALTH SERVICE

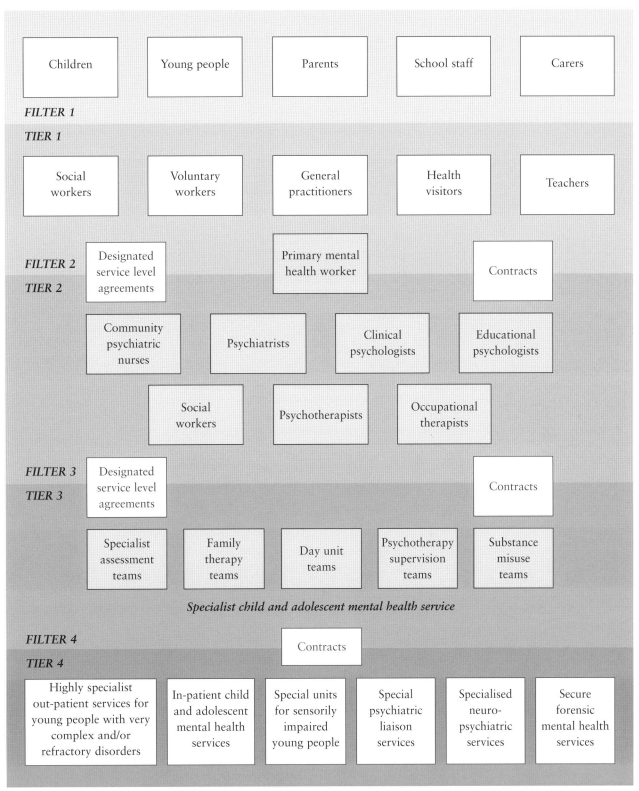

Source: based loosely on NHS Health Advisory Service (1995) *Together We Stand. The Commissioning Role and Management of Child and Adolescent Mental Health Services*, HMSO, London

APPENDIX 8

SUMMARY OF RECOMMENDATIONS GROUPED IN RELATION TO THE TARGET AUDIENCE

Key recommendations for government action

1 A Standing Commission (Advisory Committee) on the Emotional and Mental Health of Children should be established to provide the national leadership to oversee the production and implementation of the national framework and to develop a framework for cross-professional training.

2 The Government urgently needs to address the inadequacies of the current services. Legislation should establish a statutory duty for local authorities, health authorities, social services authorities and education authorities to cooperate in promoting children's mental health. The legislation should require government to develop a National Service Framework (similar to that developed for adult mental health services) for children's mental health, with clear targets for health, social services and education authorities – in order that each shall meet their responsibilities to work together and meet the needs of these children and young people. The detail of such a framework will obviously need a great deal of discussion, and we would therefore recommend the setting up of a steering group led by government in order to achieve this.

Supports for families

3 The newly established National Family and Parenting Institute should ensure that parenting initiatives are coordinated and developed effectively. A key role for the Institute must be to ensure that there are high profile media campaigns promoting public awareness of the importance of parenting, and of the vital role parents can play in promoting children's mental health.

4 The Government should give clear guidance to all employers on such issues as family-friendly working hours to enable all parents and carers to have the necessary time to spend with their children.

5 A high priority should be given to policies which promote families' abilities to promote their children's well-being. These would include
   • a clear steer from government on the effective implementation of the 'working hours directive' for all parents and carers
   • increased paid maternity and paternity leave for all parents
   • an increased commitment to a shift in resources towards lower income families.

6 The Department of Health should look at developing ways in which universal pre-birth support for all parents could begin early and be based on the assumption that preparation for parenthood is 'normal', not merely for 'at risk' families. Such support should provide an opportunity to explore emotional and relationship issues, alongside offering practical advice and support.

7 As it develops its policy on the family, the Government should address the distribution and role of health visitors. Spending plans should make adequate provision for the recruitment and training of new health visitors. In particular, areas of high morbidity or where parents are isolated because of location or ethnicity, will require higher levels of provision. In order to ensure equity of provision between communities, we would expect the Government to give clear guidance on numbers, resources and training.

8 All parenting support programmes should develop opportunities to engage fathers, particularly the most vulnerable, and to encourage them to build positive relationships with their children and increase their confidence and self-esteem.

9 The newly established National Family and Parenting Institute should ensure that parenting initiatives are coordinated and developed effectively. A key role for the Institute must be to ensure that there are high profile media campaigns promoting public awareness of the importance of parenting, and of the vital role parents can play in promoting children's mental health.

10 The National Family and Parenting Institute should be tasked with ensuring that information and support are readily available from mainstream services for parents and children during any periods of family break-up. Services set up for adults, such as Relate, should also develop support services specifically for children.

Pre-school provision

11 The Government has clearly demonstrated its commitment to the development of pre-school education for all three to four year-olds. This commitment should be extended to the provision of high quality pre-school education for all children in areas of high deprivation.

12 A coherent framework for provision for under fives, including new initiatives such as *Sure Start,* should be developed. The current demarcation between several different early years experiences, must be resolved.

13 In developing pre-school provision, the importance of children's emotional well-being, their ability to learn and to take risks should be placed centre-stage. This will require a common framework of training and practice developed for all those professionals engaged in pre-school provision to ensure that children have access to an environment that actively promotes their resilience. The variable quality of services should be addressed and standards set and monitored.

14 Within all universal pre-school provision for children, it is vital to ensure children have access to early assessment and support in relation to mental health. This will require
   • training for all staff in the skills and knowledge to promote children's emotional well-being
   • effective links between the different strands of provision envisaged by the National Child Care Strategy, *Sure Start* and National Priorities Guidance relating to child and adolescent mental health services.

15 Initiatives, such as *Sure Start,* must be backed by stable long-term funding. Without such long-term investment we fear that many extremely positive interventions will collapse after their initial pump-priming funding has ended. Interventions should also be evaluated.

Schools

16 There should be nationally funded research on school-based initiatives, long-term funding for those which work, and a programme for the dissemination of good practice.

17 League tables and other measures of schools' performance should use a range of indicators, including
   • strategies to promote children's social and emotional well-being
   • the inclusion of children and young people experiencing emotional and behavioural difficulties
   • creative and sporting achievements
   • academic results.

18 Initiatives to boost personal, social and health education in schools should include clear guidelines on how to develop programmes of emotional and social learning throughout the curriculum. OFSTED should develop the expertise to evaluate such programmes.

19 All teachers within mainstream schools should have continuing training on child development issues, an understanding of the sources of mental health difficulties and straight forward interventions, ie behaviour management techniques.

20 Each school, primary and secondary, should identify a mental health coordinator. The role would be to lead in the development of policies, practice, training and support aimed at promoting children's emotional well-being, as well as providing a link with primary care and child and adolescent mental health services.

21 Special attention must be given to the position of cultural minorities, for example, through mentoring schemes supported by members of the relevant communities.

Services for children experiencing difficulties

22 All government initiatives on children, the family and education should explicitly address mental health issues and there should be a clear cross-departmental government commitment to early intervention for children experiencing mental health problems which should include a commitment to
- develop the capacity of mainstream services, under fives provision, schools and primary care, to recognise and begin to meet the needs of children and their families when difficulties arise
- engage with, not reject, those children and families who are hardest to reach
- early intervention, not just early in the child's life, but early assessment and intervention whenever difficulties arise throughout a child's life
- long-term intervention for those children with more intractable problems
- assess the value of innovative programmes across departmental boundaries, where cost savings may be long-term and to identify long-term funding for successful interventions whether based within local authorities, health authorities, the voluntary sector or those falling between agency responsibilities.

23 The prevention of serious disturbance needs long-term and intensive commitment. There must be a commitment at both local and national level, to the development of early intervention services for older children, three plus, at risk of developing/who have developed mental health problems. Such a programme will require resourcing, in addition to that made available for *Sure Start*, *Quality Protects* and the National Priorities Guidance, in relation to children's mental health.

24 The Department of Health Research and Development programme and the Medical Research Council should give greater priority to the research and evaluation of interventions and to the effective dissemination of research to practitioners in all relevant fields.

25 Health authorities should have lead statutory responsibility for the provision of child and adolescent mental health services. Social service departments and education authorities should have specific, defined responsibilities. This would be a clear component of the proposed National Service Framework.

26 Models of good practice in coordination between a variety of agencies should be developed, evaluated and effectively disseminated to practitioners on the ground.

27 The commissioning of child and adolescent mental health services should remain with health authorities for the foreseeable future. Primary care groups need to develop the expertise to consider services in a holistic way.

28 Ring-fenced resources should be available for jointly commissioned children's services with a mental health remit, from education, health and social service departments.

Training

29 The Government should establish a cross-departmental group to develop a strategy for effective cross-professional training on children's mental health, at pre-professional and post-qualifying levels.

30 The Department of Health with The Royal College of Psychiatrists, The Royal College of Nursing and The British Psychological Society should commission a comprehensive audit of needs and an analysis of present and future staffing requirements in all services, and develop an appropriate staff development and recruitment strategy.

Services for young people

31 Within the National Service Framework, there should be a strategy on the mental health needs of young people to address
- the funding and location of preventive work with young people ensuring that innovative models of practice gain access to appropriate long-term funding
- the promotion of effective practice in meeting the needs of young people
- ways and settings which young people find acceptable
- ensuring that services for young people are operating across tiers
- access to specialist support and supervision from mental health services for community-based services working with vulnerable young people
- the gap between child and adults' services
- specialist services, eg for eating disorders and young people who self-harm.

32 We add our voice to those of others that there needs to be a national underpinning of the role and structure of the youth service.

33 The current inconsistency of youth service provision must also be resolved. It is vital that preventive services are given a clear statutory and funding basis.

34 The practice of placing young people under 18 on adult wards must cease, and greater care should be given to the provision of appropriate in-patient provision for under 25 year-olds.

35 We recommend that the new arrangements proposed by the Government in relation to 16-18 year-olds in care, which are aimed at developing their life skills and clarifying the responsibilities for their financial support, should be extended to young people up to 21.

36 Accessible, mainstream youth services, targeted at vulnerable groups, should be provided, with additional, specialist support and advocacy services for young people who have been looked after.

37 We believe that attention must be urgently given to the mental health needs of young people in young offender institutes and in prisons.
- Full initial assessments must be carried out on all young prisoners. Those who arrive with warnings concerning their vulnerability, or who exhibit these signs to reception staff, should be dealt with as a priority.
- For those young people who require it, the full range of services should be made available from trained mental health nurses, clinical psychologists, occupational therapists and others who form part of the normal mental health care team within the National Health Service.

In addition to this, we recommend that
- the Youth Justice Board should become the commissioning authority for all custodial provision for those under 18 (as the Government has suggested)

- the Board should require the operators to work to clear standards of provision and performance, based on the Children Act and the UN Convention and at least equivalent to those of the NHS in matters of health care and treatment
- young offender institutions should be inspected by joint teams with members from each of the relevant professions, reporting to the Youth Justice Board
- these institutions should, as soon as practicable, be removed from the Prison Service and the prisons estate, and placed under separate, specialised management with suitable mechanisms of accountability.

Key recommendations for social service authorities

1 The role of local authorities in providing universal services should be strengthened, and definitions of children in need should be interpreted to include children at risk of, and experiencing, mental health problems.

2 The role of social service departments, with other local authority departments and agencies, eg health, police, probation and the voluntary sector, should be strengthened using Children's Services Plans to create a network of accessible and effective preventive services.

3 There should open access or self-referral to parent support services. Such services should be able to draw support and advice from more specialist services, in order to meet the differing levels of need, and, where appropriate, refer on to specialist services.

4 All parenting support programmes should develop opportunities to engage fathers, particularly the most vulnerable, and to encourage them to build positive relationships with their children and increase their confidence and self-esteem.

5 There should be further development and evaluation of models of preventive practice by mainstream social work provision, in relation to families whose children are at risk of developing mental health problems.

6 Models of good practice in coordination between a variety of agencies should be developed, evaluated and effectively disseminated to the practitioners on the ground.

7 Ring-fenced resources should be available for jointly commissioned children's services with a mental health remit, from education, health and social service departments.

8 Each area needs to develop in-patient facilities for women who are severely mentally ill and their newborn babies, staffed by multidisciplinary teams, whose members will need to possess special skills and understanding.

9 It is important that better understanding and closer cooperation between adult and children's services is developed. Whilst we believe that it is appropriate for child and adolescent mental health services to be located within children's services, such a demarcation could lead to an increasing gulf between child and adult services. We would want to see developed
- specialist posts based in social services departments, child and adolescent mental health services and adult psychiatry which are specifically linked to maternity and post-natal services
- agreements between health and social services to focus resources jointly for mentally ill parents.

10 A coherent framework for provision for under fives, including initiatives such as *Sure Start*, should be developed. The current demarcation of different early years experiences, must be resolved.

11 In developing pre-school provision, the importance of children's emotional well-being, their ability to learn and to take risks should be placed centre-stage. This will require a common framework of training and practice developed for all those professionals engaged in pre-school provision to ensure that children have access to an environment that actively promotes their resilience. The variable quality of services should be addressed and standards set and monitored.

12 Within all universal pre-school provision for children, it is vital to ensure children have access to early assessment and support in relation to mental health. This will require
  • training for all staff in the skills and knowledge to promote children's emotional well-being
  • effective links between the different strands of provision envisaged by the National Child Care Strategy, *Sure Start* and National Priorities Guidance relating to child and adolescent mental health services.

13 Preventive interventions must begin early, be long-term and directed at risk factors, addressing those disorders where 'at risk' populations have been identified by research. Programmes must be long-term to have lasting effects and be evaluated.

14 The prevention of serious disturbance needs long-term and intensive commitment. There must be a commitment at both local and national level, to the development of early intervention services for older children, three plus, at risk of developing/who have developed mental health problems. Such a programme will require resourcing, in addition to that made available for *Sure Start, Quality Protects* and the National Priorities Guidance relating to children's mental health.

15 The mental health of all children entering care should be assessed, where necessary, by a psychiatrist or a psychologist, and they should be offered appropriate treatment and support.

16 Family, school and community links should be maintained and encouraged, where appropriate, with greater emphasis on supporting families, before, during and after children are 'looked after'.

17 As laid out in *Quality Protects*, authorities must make every effort to ensure that children have as few placements as possible.

18 Foster parents should be given training to enable them to manage difficulties and maintain placements.

19 Every young person in care should have an independent advocate or befriender during their entire period in care.

20 A key part of the service agreement of child and adolescent mental health services should be that they provide appropriate services for looked-after children.

21 There must be clear responsibility at a local level for the development of services for vulnerable young people which are fully coordinated across the tiers.

22 We recommend that the new arrangements proposed by the Government in relation to 16-18 year-olds in care, which are aimed at developing their life skills and clarifying the responsibilities for their financial support, should be extended to young people up to 21.

23 Accessible mainstream youth services, targeted at vulnerable groups should be provided, with additional, specialist support and advocacy services for young people who have been looked after.

24 Joint planning structures, and arrangements for interagency working must take account of young people in families where parents have problems. Children's Services Plans and joint planning groups could play an essential role, for example child and adolescent mental health services can have a useful input into substance misuse services, but are unlikely to do so unless the planning system supports this.

25 Within the National Service Framework, there should be a strategy on the mental health needs of young people to address
  • the funding and location of preventive work with young people ensuring that innovative models of practice gain access to appropriate long-term funding
  • the promotion of effective practice in meeting the needs of young people
  • ways and settings which young people find acceptable
  • ensuring that services for young people are operating across tiers
  • access to specialist support and supervision from mental health services for community-based services working with vulnerable young people
  • the gap between child and adults' services
  • specialist services, eg for eating disorders and young people who self-harm.

26 We recommend as a priority for further work on services for young people
  • the development, evaluation and promotion of examples of innovative practice
  • a commitment to long-term core funding of those services which can demonstrate effectiveness
  • the development of a national strategy for the training of professionals working with young people.

27 Parents of children experiencing mental health problems and young people must be consulted with and, where appropriate, involved in the development of services.

Key recommendations for health authorities, trusts and general practitioners

1 The Government urgently needs to address the inadequacies of the current services. Legislation should establish a statutory duty for local authorities, health authorities, social services authorities and education authorities to cooperate in promoting children's mental health. The legislation should require government to develop a National Service Framework (similar to that developed for adult mental health services) for children's mental health, with clear targets for health, social services and education authorities – in order that each shall meet their responsibilities to work together and meet the needs of these children and young people. The detail of such a framework will obviously need a great deal of discussion, and we would therefore recommend the setting up of a steering group led by government in order to achieve this.

2 A public health model for tackling children's mental health should be developed. This would mean acknowledging the importance of universal health promotion measures, including policies to reduce social inequalities. There should be a universal network of open access services linked to targeted services for those at risk.

3 The commissioning of child and adolescent mental health services should remain with health authorities for the foreseeable future. Primary care groups need to develop the expertise to consider services in a holistic way.

4 Universal services should be developed that have a clear focus on promoting mental health and which are developed from a clear community empowerment perspective. Such services can be time consuming and costly to develop, but unless help and support are developed in partnership with communities enabling families to promote their children's well-being, those who are the most vulnerable will continue to fail to access help and support.

Prevention/early intervention

5 Preventive interventions must begin early and be directed at risk factors, addressing those disorders where 'at risk' populations have been identified by research. Programmes must be long-term to have lasting effects.

6 The Department of Health should look at developing ways in which universal pre-birth support for all parents should begin early and be based on the assumption that preparation for parenthood is 'normal', not merely for 'at risk' families. Such support should provide an opportunity to explore emotional and relationship issues, alongside offering practical advice and support.

7 The training of all health visitors and midwives must give attention to mental health issues. Specialist training and supervision from mental health specialists should be available for health visitors to work with parents and children experiencing mental health problems.

8 Health visitors should screen all new mothers for post-natal illness and be trained in short-term interventions for post-natal depression.

9 It is important that structured programmes of home visiting are developed for families at risk. Such programmes should work in partnership with parents, offering practical support and help, and engage in 'active listening'. They should be able to offer short-term therapeutic interventions for those families displaying early problems, to encourage parents to develop other social supports and to be able to refer those parents or children who require it onto more specialist provision.

10 A coherent framework for provision for under fives, including initiatives such as *Sure Start,* should be developed. The current demarcation of different early years experiences must be resolved.

11 In developing pre-school provision, the importance of children's emotional well-being, their ability to learn and to take risks should be placed centre-stage. This will require a common framework of training and practice developed for all those professionals engaged in pre-school provision to ensure that children have access to an environment that actively promotes their resilience. The variable quality of services should be addressed and standards set and monitored.

12 Within all universal pre-school provision for children, it is vital to ensure children have access to early assessment and support in relation to mental health. This will require
   • training for all staff in the skills and knowledge to promote children's emotional well-being
   • effective links between the different strands of provision envisaged by the National Child Care Strategy, *Sure Start* and National Priorities Guidance relating to child and adolescent mental health services.

13 Each area needs to develop in-patient facilities for women who are severely mentally ill and their newborn babies, staffed by multidisciplinary teams, whose members will need to possess special skills and understanding.

14 It is important that better understanding and closer cooperation between adult and children's services is developed. Whilst we believe that it is appropriate for child and adolescent mental health services to be located within children's services, such a demarcation could lead to an increasing gulf between child and adult services. We would want to see developed

- specialist posts based in social services departments, child and adolescent mental health services and adult psychiatry which are specifically linked to maternity and post-natal services
- agreements between health and social services to focus resources jointly for mentally ill parents.

General practitioners and primary health care

15 General practitioners should become more proactive in the assessment and early intervention of children experiencing mental health problems. This would require

- training for every general practitioner in 'everyday child mental health' difficulties
- the development of active partnerships between general practitioners and specialist mental health services
- the further development and evaluation of models of effective practice in this area
- long-term funding and support of community-based services working in partnership with general practitioner practices.

16 The role of primary mental health workers needs developing nationally. Such a role can function equally effectively within a single general practitioner practice or group of practices, providing that adequate funding, an effective support network and links with other agencies are available.

Child and adolescent mental health services

17 Health authorities should have lead statutory responsibility for the provision of child and adolescent mental health services. Social service departments and education authorities should have specific, defined responsibilities. This would be a clear component of the proposed National Service Framework.

18 Models of good practice in coordination between a variety of agencies should be developed, evaluated and effectively disseminated to practitioners on the ground.

19 Ring-fenced resources should be available for jointly commissioned children's services with a mental health remit, from education, health and social service departments.

20 We support the Government's intention to make children's service planning a duty on local authorities as a whole, and the extension of local authorities' role to bring together agencies embracing children at risk of social exclusion.

21 The Department of Health Research and Development programme and the Medical Research Council should give greater priority to research and the evaluation of interventions and to the dissemination of research to practitioners in all fields.

22 A key part of the service agreement of child and adolescent mental health services should be that they provide appropriate services for looked-after children.

23 We urge the Department of Health to ensure the implementation of the Health Select Committee's recommendation that named medical advisers should be responsible for the oversight of the mental health of each child in care. We also endorse the Royal College of Nursing's recommendation that each residential home should have a named nurse, or that each home should be required to have formal links with local primary health care teams.

Services for young people

24 There must be clear responsibility at a local level for the development of services for vulnerable young people which are fully coordinated across the tiers.

25 Joint planning structures, and arrangements for interagency working must take account of young people in families where parents have problems. Children's Services Plans and joint planning groups could play an essential role, for example child and adolescent mental health services can have a useful input into substance misuse services, but are unlikely to do so unless the planning system supports this.

26 Within the National Service Framework, there should be a strategy on the mental health needs of young people to address
   • the funding and location of preventive work with young people ensuring that innovative models of practice gain access to appropriate long-term funding
   • the promotion of effective practice in meeting the needs of young people
   • ways and settings which young people find acceptable
   • ensuring that services for young people are operating across tiers
   • access to specialist support and supervision from mental health services for community-based services working with vulnerable young people
   • the gap between child and adults' services
   • specialist services, eg for eating disorders and young people who self-harm.

27 We recommend as a priority for further work on services for young people
   • the development, evaluation and promotion of examples of innovative practice
   • a commitment to long-term core funding of those services which can demonstrate effectiveness
   • the development of a national strategy for the training of professionals working with young people.

28 The practice of placing young people under 18 on adult wards must cease, and greater care given to the provision of appropriate in-patient provision for under 25 year-olds.

29 We believe that attention must be urgently given to the mental health needs of young people in young offender institutes and in prisons.
   • Full initial assessments must carried out on all young people. Those young prisoners who arrive with warnings concerning their vulnerability, or who exhibit these signs to reception staff, should be dealt with as a priority.
   • For those young people who require it, the full range of services should be made available from trained mental health nurses, clinical psychologists, occupational therapists and others who form part of the normal mental health care team within the National Health Service.
   In addition to this, we recommend that
   • the Youth Justice Board should become the commissioning authority for all custodial provision for those under 18 (as the Government has suggested)
   • the Board should require the operators to work to clear standards of provision and performance, based on the Children Act and the UN Convention and at least equivalent to those of the NHS in matters of health care and treatment
   • young offender institutions should be inspected by joint teams with members from each of the relevant professions, reporting to the Youth Justice Board
   • these institutions should, as soon as practicable, be removed from the Prison Service and the prisons estate, and placed under separate, specialised management with suitable mechanisms of accountability.

30 Parents of children experiencing mental health problems and young people must be consulted with and where appropriate involved in the development of services.

Key recommendations for local education authorities and schools

Pre-school provision

1 A coherent framework of provision for under fives, including new initiatives such as *Sure Start*, should be developed. The current demarcation between several different early years experiences, must be resolved.

2 In developing pre-school provision, the importance of children's emotional well-being, their ability to learn and to take risks should be placed centre-stage. This will require a common framework of training and practice developed for all those professionals engaged in pre-school provision to ensure that children have access to an environment that actively promotes their resilience. The variable quality of services should be addressed and standards set and monitored.

3 Within all universal pre-school provision for children, it is vital to ensure children have access to early assessment and support in relation to mental health. This will require
- training for all staff in the skills and knowledge to promote children's emotional well-being
- effective links between the different strands of provision envisaged by the National Child Care Strategy, *Sure Start* and National Priorities Guidance relating to child and adolescent mental health services.

4 Preventive interventions must begin early, be long-term and directed at risk factors, addressing those disorders where 'at risk' populations have been identified by research. Programmes must be long-term to have lasting effects and be evaluated.

Schools and colleges

5 All agencies, statutory and voluntary, working with children and young people, and particularly those working with children and young people at risk, should develop programmes of emotional and social learning within all aspects of their work.

6 Schools should be encouraged, through appropriate funding and the availability of specialist support and training to engage more fully in early intervention work with children experiencing mental health problems. Such work will be further facilitated by a culture which encourages and supports the philosophy of schools educating the 'whole child'.

7 Special attention needs to be given to the position of cultural minorities, for example through mentoring schemes, supported by members of the relevant communities.

8 The National Family and Parenting Institute should be tasked with ensuring that information and support are readily available from mainstream services for parents and children during any periods of family break-up. Services set up for adults, such as Relate, should also develop support services specifically for children.

9 League tables and other measures of schools performance should use a range of indicators, including
- strategies to promote children's social and emotional well-being
- a commitment to the inclusion of children and young people experiencing emotional and behavioural difficulties

- creative and sporting achievements
- academic results.

10 Each school, primary and secondary, should identify a mental health coordinator. The role would be to lead in the development of policies, practice, training and support aimed at promoting children's emotional well-being, as well as providing a link with primary care and child and adolescent mental health services.

11 Peer support schemes should be developed in all schools as part of a 'whole school' commitment to pupil support and antibullying policies, and programmes. Funding for such schemes should be made widely available.

12 Initiatives to boost personal, social and health education in schools should include clear guidelines as to how to develop programmes of emotional and social learning throughout the curriculum. OFSTED should develop the expertise to evaluate such programmes.

13 After and out-of-school initiatives, particularly those including arts, sports and outdoor pursuits including outdoor adventure, should be more widely available. They should focus on developing children's emotional and social skills, and are especially important within disadvantaged areas.

14 The recommendations of the Subgroup on Emotional and Behavioural Difficulties to the National Advisory Group on Special Educational Needs should be expanded to include children and young people experiencing mental health problems.
- In particular, it is important that all schools must be given guidance and training on developing whole school practice in relation to children with emotional and behavioural difficulties, and this should be extended to promoting children's mental health. This must be backed up with suitable professional development opportunities for teachers in mainstream settings.
We support the development of a simplified special educational needs code of practice. Within this, we would want to ensure that the needs of children with mental health problems are met through
- effective early assessments
- appropriate school-based interventions
- effective support from external agencies, in particular child and adolescent mental health services and other support services within education services, health authorities and social services.

15 There should be nationally-funded research on school-based initiatives, long-term funding for those which work, and a programme for the dissemination of good practice.

16 All teachers within mainstream schools should have continuing training on child development issues, an understanding of the sources of mental health difficulties and straight forward interventions, ie behaviour management techniques.

17 The focus of the role of educational psychologists should shift away from a focus on the statementing process, towards offering schools advice on interventions, programme planning/supervision and direct therapeutic interventions with the child/family in relation to mental health. In order for educational psychologists to deliver this, there must be an increase in their numbers. Currently, many local authority psychology services are operating below Warnock (1981) staffing levels of 1:3,000. Many are still operating below the level of 1:5,000 – this target as a minimum must be met.

18 Ring-fenced resources should be available for jointly commissioned children's services with a mental health remit, from education, health and social service departments.

19 We support the Government's intention to make children's service planning a duty on local authorities as a whole, and the extension of local authorities role to bring together agencies embracing children at risk of social exclusion. We recommend that within this, local authorities have a duty to ensure that the needs of children and young people experiencing mental health problems are given attention. Such a duty should also binding on health and education authorities.

Key recommendations for the voluntary sector

1 Universal services should be developed that have a clear focus on promoting mental health and which are developed from a clear community empowerment perspective. Such services can be time consuming and costly to develop, but unless help and support are developed in partnership with communities enabling families to promote their children's well-being, those who are the most vulnerable will continue to fail to access help and support.

2 The National Family and Parenting Institute should be tasked with ensuring that information and support are readily available from mainstream services for parents and children during any periods of family break-up. Services set up for adults, such as Relate, should also develop support services specifically for children.

3 All agencies, statutory and voluntary, working with children and young people, particularly those working with children and young people at risk, should develop programmes of emotional and social learning within all aspects of their work.

4 All parenting support programmes should develop opportunities to engage fathers, particularly the most vulnerable, and to encourage them to build positive relationships with their children and increase their confidence and self-esteem.

5 There should open access or self-referral to parent support services. Such services should be able to draw support and advice from more specialist services, in order to meet the differing levels of need, and where appropriate, refer on to specialist services.

6 The newly established National Family and Parenting Institute should ensure that parenting initiatives are coordinated and developed effectively. A key role for the Institute must be to ensure that there are high profile media campaigns promoting public awareness of the importance of parenting, and of the vital role parents can play in promoting children's mental health.

7 A coherent framework of provision for under fives, including new initiatives such as *Sure Start,* should be developed. The current demarcation between several different early years experiences, must be resolved.

8 In developing pre-school provision, the importance of children's emotional well-being, their ability to learn and to take risks should be placed centre-stage. This will require a common framework of training and practice developed for all those professionals engaged in pre-school provision to ensure that children have access to an environment that actively promotes their resilience. The variable quality of services should be addressed and standards set and monitored.

9 Within all universal pre-school provision for children, it is vital to ensure children have access to early assessment and support in relation to mental health. This will require
   • training for all staff in the skills and knowledge to promote children's emotional well-being
   • effective links between the different strands of provision envisaged by the National Child Care Strategy, *Sure Start* and National Priorities Guidance relating to child and adolescent mental health services.

10 Preventive interventions must begin early, be long-term and directed at risk factors, addressing those disorders where 'at risk' populations have been identified by research. Programmes must be long-term to have lasting effects and be evaluated.

11 After and out-of-school initiatives, particularly those including arts, sports and outdoor pursuits, including outdoor adventure, should be more widely available. They should focus on developing children's emotional and social skills, and are especially important within disadvantaged areas.

12 Accessible, mainstream youth services, targeted at vulnerable groups, should be provided, with additional, specialist support and advocacy services for young people who have been looked after.

13 We add our voice to those of others that there needs to be a national underpinning of the role and structure of the youth service.

14 We recommend that, as part of the National Service Framework, a national strategy be developed on the mental health needs of young people (16-25) to ensure these are addressed as a priority.

15 The current inconsistency of youth service provision must be resolved. It is vital that preventive services are given a clear statutory and funding basis.

16 We recommend as a priority for further work on services for young people
   • the development, evaluation and promotion of examples of innovative practice
   • a commitment to long-term core funding of those services which can demonstrate effectiveness
   • the development of a national strategy for the training of professionals working with young people.

17 Parents of children experiencing mental health problems and young people must be consulted with and where appropriate involved in the development of services.

Key recommendations for the criminal justice system

1 We believe that attention must be urgently given to the mental health needs of young people in young offender institutes and in prisons.
   • Full initial assessments must be carried out on all young people. Those young prisoners who arrive with warnings concerning their vulnerability, or who exhibit these signs to reception staff, should be dealt with as a priority.
   • For those young people who require it, the full range of services should be made available from trained mental health nurses, clinical psychologists, occupational therapists and others who form part of the normal mental health care team within the National Health Service.
   In addition to this, we recommend that
   • the Youth Justice Board should become the commissioning authority for all custodial provision for those under 18 (as the Government has suggested)

- the Board should require the operators to work to clear standards of provision and performance, based on the Children Act and the UN Convention and at least equivalent to those of the NHS in matters of health care and treatment
- young offender institutions should be inspected by joint teams with members from each of the relevant professions, reporting to the Youth Justice Board
- these institutions should, as soon as practicable, be removed from the Prison Service and the prisons estate, and placed under separate, specialised management with suitable mechanisms of accountability.

Key recommendations for professional and training bodies

1 The Government should establish a cross-departmental group to develop a strategy for effective cross-professional training on children's mental health, at pre-professional and post-qualifying levels.

2 The Department of Health with The Royal College of Psychiatrists, The Royal College of Nursing and The British Psychological Society should commission a comprehensive audit of needs and an analysis of present and future staffing requirements in all services, and develop an appropriate staff development and recruitment strategy.

3 The training of all health visitors and midwives must give attention to mental health issues. Specialist training and supervision from mental health specialists should be available for health visitors to work with parents and children experiencing mental health problems.

4 All teachers within mainstream schools should have continuing training on child development issues, an understanding of the sources of mental health difficulties and straight forward interventions, ie behaviour management techniques.

5 General practitioners should become more proactive in the assessment and early intervention of children experiencing mental health problems. This would require
- training for every general practitioner in 'everyday child mental health' difficulties
- the development of active partnerships between general practitioners and specialist mental health services
- the further development and evaluation of models of effective practice in this area
- long-term funding and support of community-based services working in partnership with general practitioner practices.

6 We recommend as a priority for further work on services for young people
- the development, evaluation and promotion of examples of innovative practice
- a commitment to long-term core funding of those services which can demonstrate effectiveness
- the development of a national strategy for the training of professionals working with young people.

APPENDIX 9
FURTHER READING

Alderson, P et al (1996) *What works? Effective social interventions in child welfare.* Report of a conference organised by Barnardos and the Social Science Research Unit held on 11 March 1994

Acheson, D (1998) *Independent Inquiry into Inequalities in Health Report* The Stationery Office, London

Armstrong, C Hill, M and Secker, J (1998) *Listening to Children* Mental Health Foundation, London

Association of Directors of Social Services Children and Families Committee (1997) *Investing in the Future of Children and Families, the Contribution of Personal Social Services*

The Audit Commission (1994) *Seen But Not Heard: Coordinating Community Child Health and Social Services for Children in Need* HMSO, London

Audit Commission (1996) *Misspent Youth. Young People and Crime* HMSO, London

Ball, M (1998) School Inclusion. *The school, the family and the community* Joseph Rowntree Foundation, York

Biehal, N Clayden, J Stein, M Wade, J (1995) *Moving On: Young people and leaving care schemes* HMSO, London

Communities That Care (UK) (1997) *A new kind of prevention programme*

Department of Health (1997) *Child and Adolescent Mental Health Services; Report of the Health Select Committee Proceedings* HMSO, London

Department of Health (1997) Government Response to the Reports of the Health Committee on Health Services for Children and Young People, Session 1996-7: Child and Adolescent Mental Health Services (26-1) HMSO, London

Department of Health (1992) *Health of the Nation*

Durlak, J A (1995) *School-based Prevention Programmes for Children and Adolescents* Sage, Thousand Oaks

Farrington, D P (1996) *Understanding and Preventing Youth Crime* Joseph Rowntree Foundation

Fonagy, P (1998) *Early Influences on Development and Social Inequalities* paper for Sir Donald Acheson's Independent Inquiry into Inequalities in Health

Health Education Authority (1998) *Mental Health Promotion: a quality Framework* London HEA

Goleman, D (1996) *Emotional Intelligence. Why it Can Matter More than IQ* Bloomsbury, London

Goepfert, M Webster, J and Seeman, M (eds) (1996) *Parental Psychiatric Disorder. Distressed Parents and their families* Cambridge University Press

Guralnik, M (ed) (1997) *The Effectiveness of Early Intervention* Brookes, Baltimore

Howard League for Penal Reform (1995) *Banged Up, Beaten Up, Cutting Up* Report of the Howard League Commission of Inquiry into Violence in Penal Institutions for teenagers under 18 Howard League, London

Kurtz, Z Thornes, R Wollkind, S (1994) *Services for the Mental Health of Young People in England: A National Review* Maudsley Hospital and South Thames (West) RHA, London

Kurtz, Z Thornes, R Wollkind, S (1995) *Services for the Mental Health of Children and Young People in England: assessment of needs and unmet need* report to the Department of Health, London

Kurtz, Z (1996) *Treating Children Well* Mental Health Foundation, London

Law, S (1998) *Hear Me* Mental Health Foundation, London

Lloyd, E et al (1997) *Today and Tomorrow: Investing in our Children* Barnardos, Essex

MacDonald, G and Roberts, H (1995) *What Works in the Early Years? Effective interventions for children and their families in health, social welfare, education and child protection part III* Barnardos, Essex

NHS Health Advisory Service (1995) *Together We Stand. The Commissioning Role and Management of Child and Adolescent Mental Health Services* HMSO, London

NHS Advisory Service (1996) *Children and Young People. Substance Misuse Services. Commissioning and Providing Services for Young People who use and misuse substances* HMSO, London

Pugh, G De'Ath, E and Smith, C (1994) *Confident Parents, Confident Children. Policy and practice in parenting education and support* National Children's Bureau, London

Rodgers, B and Pryor, J (1998) *Divorce and Separation. The Outcomes for Children* Joseph Rowntree Foundation, York

Roth, A and Fonagy, P (1996) *What Works for Whom: A critical review of psychotherapy research* Guildford Press, New York

Rutter, M 1975 *Helping Troubled Children* Penguin

Rutter, M (1985) *Resilience in the face of adversity. Protective factors and resistance to psychiatric disorder* British Journal of Psychiatry vol 147 pp598-611

Rutter, M Giller, H Hagell, A (1998) *Antisocial behaviour by Young People. A Major New Review of the Research* Cambridge University Press

Rutter, M and Smith, D J (1995) *Psychosocial Disorders in Young People. Time trends and their causes* John Wiley & Sons Ltd, Chichester

Smith, C (1996) *Developing Parenting Programmes* National Children's Bureau, London

Stein, M (1997) *What Works in Leaving Care* Barnardos

Utting, D (1995) *Family and Parenthood: supporting families, preventing breakdown* Joseph Rowntree Foundation, York

Wallace, S A, Crown, J M, Cox A D, Berger, M (1995) *Epidemiologically-based Needs Assessment; Child and Adolescent Mental Health* Wessex Institute of Public Health

Her Majesty's Inspectorate of Prisons for England and Wales (1997) *Young Prisoners: A Thematic Review of Prisons* by HM Chief Inspector of Prisons for England and Wales Home Office, London